PUBLISHED FOR THE TRUSTEES OF
THE NATIONAL MARITIME MUSEUM BY

LONDON HER MAJESTY'S STATIONERY OFFICE

G000153492

FROM VIKING SHIP TO *VICTORY*

Excavation of the Skuldelev Viking Age wrecks inside coffer-dam.

Scarcely anywhere on the face of the earth is there a cultural area which can illustrate the history of its shipbuilding in such detail as can the Nordic area. This is true first and foremost of the Viking age, about 1000 years ago, when Nordic seamen traded and made war from Russia and Byzantium in the south east to Greenland and Vinland in the north west. This expansion was made possible by the development of the seaworthy, swift and efficient Viking ship, and many thrilling details of this history are illustrated in the copious source material provided by archaeological finds of ships, by sagas' texts of laws, by rune-stones and tapestries.

The celebrated Norse burial ships from Gokstad and Oseberg which were excavated in 1880 and 1904 on the west side of the Oslo fjord are regarded today as classic examples of Viking ships. These splendid vessels of 800–900 AD served as a last resting place for royal persons, and the fortunate circumstance that the ships in the graves were covered by a compact layer of clay has preserved the woodwork incredibly well. Other burial ships lay in less fortunate situations; of the ship in the chieftain's grave from Ladby in Denmark (excavated during 1935) there remained only the impression in the earth, together with the long rows of iron nails.

The best idea of the scope of shipbuilding in the Viking Age is, however, given by the five ships of the Skuldelev find sunk in the Roskilde fjord, Denmark, to block the channel and thus protect Roskilde some time in the first half of the 11th century. They were recovered after draining and excavation in 1962. The five ships are two merchant ships, two war ships, and a ferry or fishing boat.

Ships and seafaring are amongst the favourite themes of the Icelandic saga. In most cases it is difficult to distinguish between what is original in the text of the saga, and contemporary with the events described, and later additions made when they were written down in the 13th and 14th centuries. But taken as a whole the sagas give much valuable information about shipbuilding in the saga period. In addition, the texts of some of the oldest laws which have been preserved, eg, the Guta law, can throw some light on ships and navigation in the early middle ages.

Ships are among the stone carvers' favourite motifs on rune-stones and on the numerous splendid carved stones from Gotland. On most of them the Viking ship is seen under full sail. Lastly we must mention that priceless treasure, the Bayeux Tapestry, a 70-metre long series of illustrations, embroidered about 900 years ago in commemoration of William the Conqueror's campaign against England in 1066. In clear outlines and with much vivid detail, this describes the preparations for the campaign, the building of ships for the invasion fleet, the crossing and landing, and the battle of Hastings.

Bayeux

The student of the days when the *Victory* sailed the seas has a wealth of material to draw upon. There are draughts of the ships in the National Maritime Museum, many with the designer's and master shipwright's notes for modifications still visible on them. There are superb models, many originally built for the Navy Board, at Greenwich and at the Science Museum, South Kensington. The log of the *Victory* and her muster-roll, together with innumerable documents, private logs, confidential instructions and reports are all carefully preserved in archives, museums and the Public Record Office. Moreover, the second half of the 18th century saw the publication of instructional books written for shipwrights and seamen; all provide further authentic information. Prints and pictures are legion and portraits of the men who commanded the ships are nearly as numerous.

But it is the survival of the *Victory* herself which most dramatically re-creates the world of oak and hemp. Her present resting-place in the ancient No.2 graving dock at Portsmouth was only achieved after a long career during which destruction threatened again and again. For a long period after her launch in 1765 the *Victory* lay in the Medway. In 1778 she was at last fitted out for duty at sea. Only ten years later the first of many extensive re-fits was necessary; these re-fits could take years to complete. Between 1797 and 1800 she again lay in the Medway, her yards and upper-masts sent down, serving as a hospital ship for the poor wretches sent from the prison-hulks.

It was only a short time before she was again on active service, but in the years 1801–3 she again had 'large repairs'. It was on this occasion that the open stern galleries, so beloved by commanders, were enclosed and the rigging-channels moved from below to above the upper gun-deck ports where they were less vulnerable. After her finest hour at Trafalgar, battered and dismasted, she was nearly lost when under tow to the safety of Gibraltar. She was once again repaired extensively at Chatham, and was re-commissioned in March 1808. Three years later, when returning from the Baltic the *Victory* survived a savage gale.

Later the same year another docking for 'large repairs' transformed her into the form in which she remained until 1922. Principal among the changes of 1811 was a building-up of her bow. Just as the traditional stern had been a point of weakness in battle, so the old square bulkhead at the bow invited attack.

The *Victory's* last sea voyage was made in 1812, at the end of which she was paid off at Portsmouth, once again for repairs in the dockyard. These lasted from 1814 until 1816. She remained there and was eventually condemned as unsound and beyond repair. However, a newspaper campaign initiated by John Poole, writing as 'Paul Pry', saved her from demolition and in 1825 she was made flagship of the Port Admiral of Portsmouth and moored in the Harbour.

In 1903, an old-iron-clad, under tow, rammed the wooden man-of-war below the waterline; only fine seamanship enabled her to be docked before foundering. An extensive survey in 1921 found her hull to be in a dangerous condition, and regrettably, handing the *Victory* over to the shipbreakers seemed the only course to be taken. But, again, a newspaper campaign and other timely intervention saved her. With immense care the Society for Nautical Research restored the *Victory* to her condition at the time of Trafalgar, now safely ashore and carefully shored up in a dry-dock. In the dry-dock at Portsmouth she survived yet another blow. A German bomb exploded under her bow in 1942, but fortunately the force was taken by the immense forebitts, and serious damage was restricted.

Small boats, Gokstad

The classification of Viking men-of-war was based on the number of oars, the decisive factor for movement and manoeuvring in battle.

The smallest class contained those boats in which each man pulled two oars. They were called *aeringr*, according to the number of oars, from four to twelve. In the Gokstad ship remains of three boats were found, two 4-oarers, *feraeringr* (Norwegian *faering*), and one 6-oarer, *sexaeringr*. The longships were called -*sessa* (benchers) according to the number of thwarts or benches, ie, the number of pairs of oars. In these ships each man pulled only one oar and, in certain

cases, there were even several men to each oar. The smallest size of ship reckoned in -*sessur* was the 13-bencher, *prettan-sessa* with 26-oars. The sizes of ships between -benchers and -oarers were described according to the number of oarsmen on either side.

The sagas are full of stories of ships and seagoing. Types of ships such as the *karfar*, *skutur*, *snekkjur*, *skeidir* and *drekar* are named several times but only with great difficulty can the quotations be combined to make a complete picture which, must be treated with great reserve. From this material we can deduce the following outline. The *karve*

(not mentioned in Danish or Swedish sources) was the private ship of a chief or a great landowner and was driven by sail and from 12 to 32 oars. The Norse burial ships from Tune, Oseberg and Gokstad were presumably of this type. The *skude* was a low, lightly built warship with 8 to 30 oars, suitable for reconnaissance. The Skuldelev ship no.5 and the Ladby ship were probably of this type. The *longships* of the war fleet, represented by Skuldelev no.2, had at least 26 oars, more often as many as 40, whilst the *storskibe* (large ships) had to have at least 50. In Denmark and Sweden, *snekke* was the normal expression for a warship, which in Norway was limited in size to about 40 oars, whilst the largest of all the *skeide* usually had 60 oars. The name *skeide* is related to the type

Carved Stone, Hunninge

of Byzantine ship known as a *skedija*.

Highest in rank was the *dragon ship* with 60 or more oars. *Ormen Lange*, (The Long Serpent) built in the winter of 999–1000, was reputed to have 34 sections (68 oars). These ships probably belonged to the world of reality. Where shall we stop?–at Håkon Jarl's 40 section ship, Bishop Håkon's 45 section ship, or at King Canute's 60 section dragon?

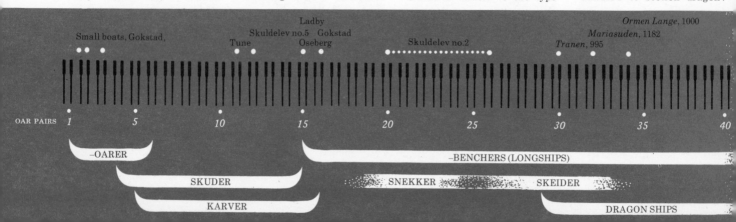

Small boats, Gokstad,

Ladby
Skuldelev no.5 Gokstad
Tune   Oseberg

Skuldelev no.2

Ormen Lange, 1000
Mariasuden, 1182
Tranen, 995

OAR PAIRS 1   5   10   15   20   25   30   35   40

–OARER

–BENCHERS (LONGSHIPS)

SKUDER

SNEKKER   SKEIDER

KARVER

DRAGON SHIPS

During the great days of the sailing men-of-war it was principally the number of guns which decided the rank of a naval vessel. The heavier the broadside a ship could hurl from its guns the more sure was a ship to gain the upper hand in an engagement. Throughout the 18th century the back-bone of the British Navy, was its ships-of-the-line. Such a ship was the *Victory*, an exceptional *elite*, at the time of her launch, in carrying at least 100 guns. Most of the ships-of-the-line were armed with 74 guns and in the 18th century only the major powers could afford to build and maintain 100-gun vessels. The *Victory* was considered superior amongst the august company of three-deckers for she could out-sail and come closer to the wind than her equals.

The largest ships-of-the-line carried the majority of their guns on three decks, hence the title of *three-deckers*, although in actual fact they had many more than that. On the *lowest gun-deck* were ranged the biggest guns of all, thirty black-painted 32 pounders, supplemented by two 12 pounders. Above this was the *middle-deck* on which were the 24 pounders, 28 in all, while on the *upper-deck* were ranged the guns throwing round-shot weighing 12 pounds. On the open quarter-deck were twelve 12 pounders.

The massive ships-of-the-line were supported by *frigates*. These began, in the 17th century, as lightly armed sailing vessels, sometimes using sweeps as auxiliary power. Sweep-ports in the sides of lightly built frigates and some smaller vessels continued until the early years of the 19th

A First-Rate at sea under reduced sail

century. Frigates developed into fast, weatherly vessels, carrying their guns on one deck. It was their duty to protect merchant-men from attack, relay messages between ships-of-the-line and act as the eyes of the fleet.

The size of the frigates and their armament tended to increase until, by the end of the days of sail, the largest of them were carrying 50 guns on one deck and a long quarter-deck.

Besides these were a wealth of smaller vessels; there were *sloops*, which were ship-rigged, lightly built and carrying about 18 guns; *brigs*, two-masted and varying in armament, some carrying only 6 guns, while others were equipped with as many as 18. Brigs could be counted by the score, but lower down the scale were an even larger host of *ketch-rigged bomb vessels*, *schooners*, *cutters* and *pulling launches* for landing troops. These were all serviced by a motley fleet of still smaller *hoys*, *lighters*, *water-boats* and *row-barges*.

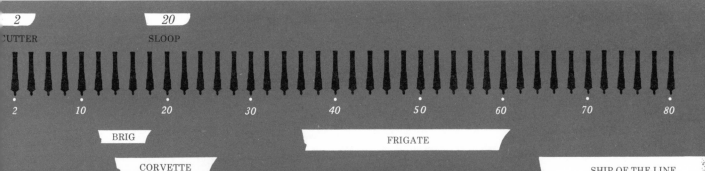

'After the battle of Avaldsnaes King Håkon made a provision in the law that the settlements along the Norwegian coast and as far inland as the salmon go, should be split up into naval regions which in their turn were divided up into counties, and for each county the number and size of the ships was laid down, which they should present when the whole fleet was called out, that is to say when a foreign force was in the land. Every calling out of the fleet was to be proclaimed by beacons on high mountain tops, and the distance between them must be such that it was possible to see from one to the other. It is said that in this way the calling out of the forces could be transmitted in seven nights from the most southern beacon in Norway to the most northerly parish in Halogaland.' (The Saga of Håkon the Good).

According to the law of the Gulathing, the Norwegian ship levy consisted of 195 × 20 benchers, 116 × 25 benchers and one 30 bencher, in all 312 ships, whilst the Danish ship levy had about 1100 ships. It was the King who called out the fleet, and all the indications are that this seaborne defence force, which in Denmark comprised 30–40,000 men, is just as old as the centralised royal power and the kingdom itself.

The fleet could be called out for the defence of the country, but also for a campaign abroad, wherever the threat might be. The campaigns against Wendland, especially those against Rygen described by Saxo, were a natural counter move against the Wends' attack on the southern part of Denmark. About 1170, after the conquest of Rygen, the fleet was reorganised so that one ship in four was always at sea ready for action with a young unmarried crew. Gradually the liability to naval service was replaced by a tax, and in 1304 the change from the *longship* to the *cog* represented a decisive break with the old traditions in Denmark. For example, Zealand had in the past equipped about 120 longships, but from 1304 AD Zealanders had to pay for the equipment of five to ten cogs.

In the year 994 Sven Forkbeard, together with Olav Trygveson's Viking fleet, ravaged southern England and extorted 16,000 pounds of silver from the citizens of London. There followed a long series of campaigns against England in the course of which King Sven's well-disciplined Viking force ravaged and took Danegeld in an ever-increasing part of the country until in 1013 England had to take him as king. In these campaigns Sven depended on professional soldiers and not on conscripts, and for the winter quartering and training of these men he built four large circular strongholds, distributed strategically over Denmark so that at the same time they could maintain the unity of the kingdom.

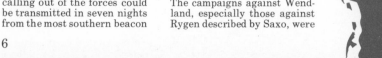

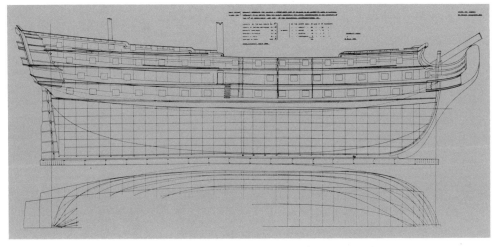

Over the years the rules changed, slowly and usually after a challenge had been presented by foreign navies.

The biggest ships-of-the-line under construction and afloat were French or Spanish, both countries with material resources comparable to Britain, and these had to be matched, if not bettered, for Britain's growing importance as a world power relied heavily on her superiority on the high seas. The building programme which was proposed in 1758 was to begin with the construction of a noble ship-of-the-line, capable of tackling any adversary afloat. This was the *Victory* whose keel was laid in June of the following year, 1759.

In December 1758 the ministers of King George II decided to ask Parliament to sanction the start of a massive naval construction programme. No less than twelve ships-of-the-line were to be built and the keels of nine of them were to be laid down immediately. Britain was on the verge of the 'Year of Victories', when on land and sea we brought to a triumphant climax the Seven Years War against France and her ally Austria.

It was the policy of Britain to cut France off from her colonies by the Navy. This policy was a demanding one which extended the resources of the sea forces to their limit.

There had to be fleets available to blockade Brest in Brittany and Toulon on the Mediterranean, to watch the Straits of Gibraltar and to protect merchant-men in the far-off Indian Ocean. Traders had to be guarded from pirates and privateers from the North Sea to the Caribbean and soldiers had to be convoyed in transports across the Atlantic.

To meet these demands the shipbuilders of the 18th century had to contend with a system of 'establishments' laid down by the authorities which rapidly became outdated. They set down in detail, from figurehead to stern-post, how ships of every size were to be built.

The draught plan of the *Victory* as she was built in 1759

Nowhere in the Norse area has any structure of a Viking shipyard been found by archaeologists although thousands of ships were built. The explanation is quite simple: shipbuilding was carried out in the open or under a lean-to shelter *(hrōf)* without the multifarious fixed equipment which we find in a present day shipyard and which can leave behind archaeological traces. Only the slipway beams on which the keel was laid were firmly fixed in the ground with large wooden pegs. But here they quickly rotted away to disappear without trace if they were not of specially strong timber. Thus Snorre the early 13th century Icelandic historian relates that the slipway beams for the *Ormen Lange* (built in the winter of 999–1000) could in his time – 200 years later – still be seen in the ground at Ladehammeren outside Nidaros, so that the length of the ship could be estimated from them.

The skilled craftsmen of a shipyard were divided by ancient custom into plank cutters *(filungar,* from *fjol =* board), and stemsmiths *(stafnasmidir* – the word 'smith' is used in Old Norse to describe anyone who is able to shape any material, whether it be iron or wood). A stem-smith received twice the wages of a plank cutter; he was the specialist, the repository of

centuries of hard-won experience never committed to writing, and it was he who determined from the store of his knowledge the proportions and the shape of the ship. He was the indispensable craftsman; but plank cutting was for anyone who could swing an axe. When work on a large vessel was to be undertaken there was a greater degree of specialisation. On the *Ormen Lange*, in addition to Torberg who was the master builder *(hofudsmidr)*, some worked as wood fellers, others as ships' carpenters or 'smiths' and some as labourers. Moreover shipbuilding was seasonal work to be undertaken in the winter and the spring; it did not take long to build a Viking ship; even one of the larger ones could be built in about three months. On the Bayeux Tapestry men are seen felling trees and cutting planks in

the woods, and engaged in the actual building work. In front of the stem of one ship stands a stem-smith who is gauging with his eye whether the run of the planking is fair: every boatbuilder will recognise this situation. In the building of wooden ships aesthetics and function unite in a very pleasing way.

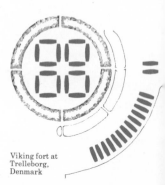

Viking fort at Trelleborg, Denmark

The British Navy had permanent bases along the south and west coast of Britain where ships for the fleet were built under direct supervision. On the banks of the Thames at Woolwich, the highest point on the river to which deep draught ships could ascend, was an ancient royal dockyard, while another was founded nearby at Deptford. Harwich, on the east coast, had its official depôt, which was maintained as long as the threat from a Dutch fleet existed.

Harwich emerged as a King's yard during the seventeenth century and owed much to the skill of Sir Anthony Deane and his mentor Samuel Pepys, famous as Secretary of the Navy and the ablest of its administrators. Pepys laid down the main rules and establishments of the Admiralty (the dimensions and standards of the equipment to which ships should be built) which in a modified form were still in use when the *Victory* was planned a century later.

The Medway river in Kent provides a wide sheltered estuary and at its head Chatham developed into a naval base. It was there that the keel of the *Victory* was laid down in 1759, nearly a century after the daring attack of the Dutch which found many royal ships laid-up undefended.

The sheltered estuaries at the back of the Isle of Wight

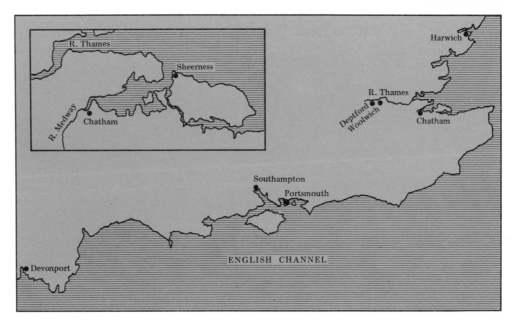

provided an excellent site for a base. The first was founded at Southampton, in the 15th century, where the Surveyor of the King's Ships administered the dockyard at the modest salary of twelvepence a day.

It was Henry VIII and his father who were the creators of the permanent naval system, including dockyards, building slipways and establishing the Navy Board of experienced executives. (Henry VIII also

developed the Thames building-yards). He moved his base from Southampton to Portsmouth, constructing what was claimed to be the first drydock in England and building heavy fortifications. It was a navy-town, founded for the navy and intended to command the Channel.

No enemy ever penetrated the waters of Portsmouth Harbour, where the *Victory* now lies in her dry-dock, although its elaborate defences on sea

and land, still to be seen, show that a French attack was often expected. Further west and founded by William III Plymouth Dock – now Devonport Dockyard – gave a refuge to the fleets patrolling the Atlantic approaches. All had good road communication with London which assisted in Admiralty supervision. Each dockyard was controlled by a Commissioner and had a Master Shipwright, working under a Senior Surveyor.

During the careful examination of every single piece of wood from the Skuldelev ships, not a single trace of a saw cut was found. Everywhere there are clear signs of axes and planes in various forms, but even in places where today a saw would obviously be used, marks are found on the surface of the wood which show that the axe has been used instead.

To an overwhelming extent the many axe marks come from the type of axe known as a *smidarøx*, in which the edge of the axe-blade is parallel to the haft. Even the smoothing of the wide oak planks has been done with such an axe. On the Bayeux Tapestry there is a plank cutter astride a plank, one end of which is inserted in a split tree trunk whilst he shapes its side with his broad axe. In the shaping of the Skuldelev ships' oak planks, an axe with a narrower blade has been used, plied with such a steady hand that when the plank was completely fashioned it did not need any additional planing or smoothing. On the other hand pine planks have been planed with an implement which reminds us of a contemporary bark-knife. The cutting axe, ie, the oblique bladed axe, is met with in many finds of the Viking period, some with a narrow blade and some with a broader blade. Is it an axe of this kind which the boatbuilder is swinging in one of the Bayeux ships? Here and there in archaeological finds a kind of narrow axe is met with which, in spite of its appearance, is not really an axe but a hafted wedge without a cutting edge. It was used for splitting off planks and had a completely straight haft. Wherever treenails had to be inserted, a hole had first to be bored with a spoon-shaped bit. It was put in a T-shaped auger with two arms with which it was turned, and a vertical shaft which was held in a block of wood against the boatbuilder's chest. This is also seen in use on the Bayeux Tapestry. Hammers and tongs were used in forging and clenching the many iron nails between the strakes. The Ladby ship had about 2,000 boat nails used in her planking.

Many axes and other implements are known from the graves of the Viking period, but it is not always possible to distinguish between the artisan's axe and that of the warrior, and in any case it is seldom that a grave yields a large selection of tools. The most important find of tools is without doubt the chest found in 1936 at Mästermyr in Gotland which contained an all-purpose artisan's tool kit, blacksmith's, locksmith's and coppersmith's tools together with those of carpenters and boatbuilders. By the Viking period most of these types of tool had taken on a form which remained unchanged until the onset of industrialisation.

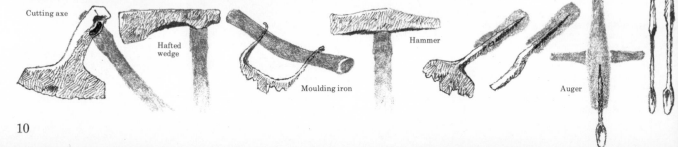

Cutting axe

Hafted wedge

Moulding iron

Hammer

Auger

Spoon bits

10

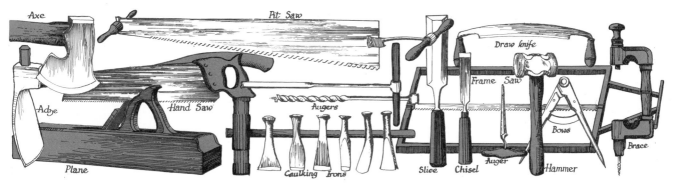

The limited range of tools used by the Vikings, and with which they performed their triumphs of craftsmanship, could be found in the substantial toolboxes of the Chatham shipwrights responsible for constructing the *Victory*. However, alongside them, made from superior steel, were many innovations, products of centuries of development. The days of cleaving and splitting logs had long since past and the production of planks and beams from logs was the task of the shipyard's sawyers.

They worked with *pit saws* and were men of heroic stamina. Logs were set up on trestles so that a man could stand upright beneath them, or alternatively in a narrow pit, where he pulled the lower end of the saw. The top-sawyer stood above and lifted the saw at each stroke and saw to it

that the sawing followed the lines marked out along the length of the trunk. Accurate sawing saved the shipwright much labour later, with *axe*, *plane* and *adze*.

The cutting tool peculiar to the shipwright was the adze. From medieval times it was used to shape the frames to the correct angle, determined by the *bevel*, hollowed the inner faces of planks to fit the frames and faired-up (or smoothed) the outer surface of the completed hull. *Cross-cut saws*, worked by two men were in constant use for all these jobs while the *compass saw* shaped the curved knees and 'hooks'. Primitive *heavy axes* for hewing, as well as *wood axes* and *hatchets*, were still in use long after the launch of the Victory. *Planes* were for finishing joints and *draw-knives* for rounding rails and spars. *Chisels*, used

by master-craftsmen, cut the cunning run of the rabbet in the keel and the scarfs which reinforced the joints in the keel and keelson.

The great range of *augers*, *awls* and *bits*, employed to bore holes for wooden trennels, iron and copper bolts and spikes, were a valued part of the ship-

wrights tool-kit. Great skill and a capacity to make haste slowly were needed to bore such holes as were required for the *Victory*'s stem bolts, some 9 feet in depth!

All the seams of the wooden vessel were caulked with *oakum*, the strands of loose, old hemp rope driven home with chisel-shaped *caulking-irons*. These were struck with the long-handled *caulking-mallet* and it was usually the task reserved for apprentices and older workmen. They stood on stagings high up against the ship's side, the sound of their blows echoing afar. Although wooden fishing-boats 60 feet in length are still built on the east and west coasts of Scotland, and many traditional skills are still used there, the whine of the electric drill and powered band-saw dominate the scene today.

Some of the types of ship in the Viking period had names derived from the kind of wood characteristically used in the ship, sometimes at an earlier stage of its development. *Aesc* (made of ash) was the name given by the English to the medium-sized Danish Viking ship. This accords with the fact that the three uppermost strakes in the 24-oarer warship in the Skuldelev find are of ash. *Espingr* (made of aspen) was a ship's boat, deriving ultimately from a hollowed out aspen trunk.

However, it was mainly oak and pine trees that were used in shipbuilding, and they were felled and converted into planks without the use of the saw. But other kinds of timber are met with in the Skuldelev ships, eg, lime, alder, birch, beech, and also willow which

was used for the treenails. For curved parts such as ribs, stems and knees, timber was chosen which had grown in the desired shape. Whenever suitable material was found for shipbuilding, it was immediately roughly hewn to shape even if it were perhaps not immediately needed. It could always be kept from drying out by being stored in water until a use for it was found. By ancient custom every peasant could take curved wood or 'crooks' from the forest if he had need of it, and also timber for a small ship. 'A man may cut, in the land leased to him, timber for a 12-oared ship or less, but not for a bigger ship or for more than one ship without the landlord giving permission. But he shall be fined if he cuts more'. (From the Law of Frostating.)

For planks, logs had to be chosen which were quite straight and free from flaws. Pine logs were split once and probably gave only two planks per trunk, whilst oak trunks were split in two, in four, and so on, right up to 32 giving wedge-shaped planks with an apex angle of 11 degrees. These radial split planks (or *cloveboards* as they are called in early medieval English customs lists) were standard materials which could be used without further shaping, for example, in house building or, after dressing and smoothing, in shipbuilding. In order to get planks 30 cm wide in this manner, an oak log had to be about 1 metre in diameter. These planks were ideal for the purpose because this radial orientation in the log combines

maximum strength with minimum shrinkage. Even today when sawing up planks for boat building, one tries to get 'quarter-sawn' boards.

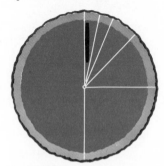

Oak is split into wedges and gives up to 32 planks, 30 cm wide, from a 1 metre diameter log

Pine is split and gives 2 planks, 30 cm wide, from a 0.4 metre diameter log

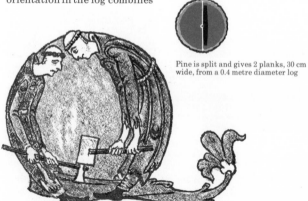

English oak reigned supreme as the basic raw material for building the British fleet. It was English oak that the master-shipwrights sought above all; it had a rugged quality superior to all others. While other oaks existed, none came up to the standards of the well-seasoned English variety. Its only disadvantage was its tendency to splinter when it was struck by round-shot; many of the wounds sustained by the gun-crews were caused in this way. Elm, because it was obtainable in long runs and could withstand immersion well, was used for keels.

'Plank' was the term used when the thickness was from 4 inches to 1½ inches and up to 12 inches in width. Below this size sawn timber was known as *boards*, while sawn timber above plank dimensions was recognised as *thick-stuff*. The great band of timber which encircled the hull of a man-of-war was a wale 8 inches thick. The transportation of felled timber by horse and wagon was difficult to undertake particularly after a spell

of wet weather. Whenever possible trees were rough-hewn and sawn to the required shape where they were felled and then brought to the royal dockyards, if it could be arranged, by sea aboard hoys; it was not unknown for it to be rafted down rivers and towed to its destination. The royal dockyards on the south coast competed with charcoal burners, who supplied the iron-smelters of the Weald with timber, as well as house-builders and private shipyards whose owners offered ready money and high prices, particularly for the grown crooked timber from hedgerow oaks.

As early as 1608 James I initiated a survey of the royal forests, at that time a huge area, and found only some 500,000 loads, or roughly 350,000 trees were available while less than half were fit for shipbuilding use. By 1783 these reserves had dropped by four-fifths. Only when this point was reached did the use of iron slowly become accepted as a possible alternative to grown wooden *knees*, *hooks*

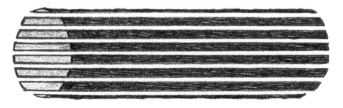

and *crooks*. The 19th century saw another innovation. Burma teak was employed in constructing ships at Bombay and some of the finest of the last wooden-walls launched were built of this water-resistant timber. Their long life undoubtedly vindicated the break with tradition.

The rapid decay of wooden hulls faced the shipwrights with their most serious challenge. Between 1690 and 1719

the inner faces of planks were charred; later it was realised that a free flow of air around a vessel's timbers was essential and the seasoning of timber for at least two years, suitably covered and carefully supervised, reduced rot. But the 'tween-decks of the *Victory* and her consorts invariably combined the sour smell of infected timber with the aroma of sweating humanity in its rank atmosphere.

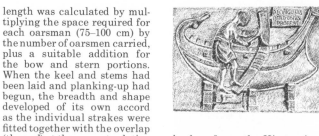

In the course of the Iron Age clinker building was developed in the Norse area to such a high technical level that the Vikings could build ships whose seaworthiness was unsurpassed and which could be fashioned at will as long, narrow, lightly built landing craft or as short, sturdy and broad cargo boats for carrying livestock and trading goods. They all have one thing in common: they were built entirely without the use of drawings such as shipwrights use today. The extensive use of working drawings is a recent phenomenon, and the shipbuilders of the Viking period certainly did not use them. They had a firm tradition of proportion and shape to which they built, inherited through a living tradition, and continuously brought up to date as a result of experience on the high seas and in battle.

When a warship was to be built, the length could be decided from the designated number of oarsmen. This length was calculated by multiplying the space required for each oarsman (75–100 cm) by the number of oarsmen carried, plus a suitable addition for the bow and stern portions. When the keel and stems had been laid and planking-up had begun, the breadth and shape developed of its own accord as the individual strakes were fitted together with the overlap (the *sud*) at the correct relative slopes. The master boatbuilder fashioned the desired shape as he worked the planks. The ribs were inserted later and they were of secondary importance, mere supporting timbers which were shaped to fit the completed shell of keel, stems and planking to strengthen it when at sea. This shell building tradition has ancient roots in the North, where it can be traced back as far as the Hjortspring boat of 4–300 BC. It is the natural thing for clinker building and even today it can be met with in its pure form in old clinker-builders workshops, but it was also used in the earliest history of the flush-laid ship of the Mediterranean. Thus Odysseus's boat, just like the Viking ships, was built as a plank shell and then lined with ribs.

Merchant ship

Stem

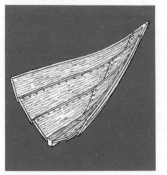

Stem with planking

Dragon ship

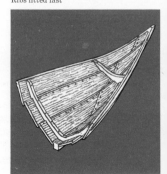

Ribs fitted last

14

The British men-of-war of the 18th century were all built from drawings. The original lines plan for the *Victory* is still in existence, held by the National Maritime Museum, together with the deck plans, undated but probably 18th century. But no records survive of the subsequent modifications, made during her long life, in 1787–8, 1800–2 and 1814–16, except for a 19th century profile. The drawings of her lines and constructional details are those drawn up by Thomas Slade in 1759 in his capacity of Senior Surveyor of the Navy. He was principal officer between 1755–71, holding office jointly from 1765 until 1771, charged with the building and repairing of the royal ships. He completed the plans of the new three-decker within six months and they were then conveyed to Chatham Dockyard, for the attention of Mr. Allen, Master Shipwright, for the work to begin immediately.

On the basis of these drawings the hull could be constructed; the sectional drawings showed how the *keel*, *stem-pieces* and *deck-beams* should be made up. The sectional drawings indicated how the thickness of the side and deck planking should vary. The dimensions of these details were laid down by the Navy Board; for any variations in them to be made by the shipwrights at the dockyard sanction had to be obtained at the highest level to avoid any possibility of weakness in the structure.

From the line-drawing a full-scale drawing on the deal-planked *mould-loft* floor, planed smooth and blackened, was drawn-up (or laid-off). For each rib a template was prepared from the drawing on the *mould-loft* floor and its shape was marked off on the rib-timber so that individual pieces could be sawn and fashioned to the desired shape and then joined together. They were then ready for erecting on the keel, laid ready on great oaken blocks, placed at intervals of 4 or 5 feet. The *Victory* was unusual in having her keel laid in a dry-dock, the Old Single Dock at Chatham, on the Medway, near the house of the admiral superintendent.

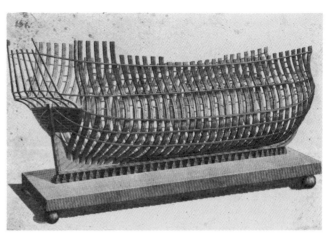

Perspective drawing of the frame timbers of a 100 gun ship

The site has long since been obliterated by modern dockyard development.

When the keel-stem and stern post and the many ribs (or frames) had been assembled into a giant skeleton in the dock the *cladding* of the ship could begin, both inboard (the ceiling) and outboard.

The use of plans, such as were drawn out in 1759 for the *Victory*, dated from the end of the 17th century. Before that period a fundamental set of rules, largely arrived at empirically, based upon the length of the proposed vessels not unlike that used for the Viking ships, was used. Models, made to scale, were also employed, from which dimensions were taken and scaled up, as they would when working from a drawing.

Very fine, contemporary models were also built of men-of-war which were constructed from plans. These were ordered for presentation to the Navy Board to demonstrate the proposed vessels as vividly as possible. The model of the *Victory* in the National Maritime Museum (No.1765–1) is one of these and shows how she appeared when launched. Another, on a smaller scale, is a frame-model, showing the construction and is also contemporary with her building at Chatham.

The drawings from which the shape of the frames were taken

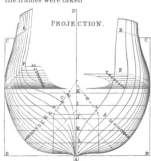

Nydam

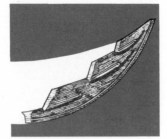

Gokstad small boat

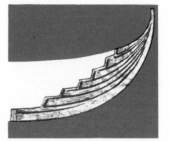

Skuldelev no.3

Graffiti, Oseberg

The oak keel was the backbone of the Viking ship. It might be deep and sturdy as in the Gokstad ship which was intended for use in the deep Norwegian fjords, or shallow, as in the Skuldelev ships which were built for shallow shores. But, whatever the circumstances, the keel was a distinctive characteristic of the Norse ship. The name of the shiptype *ceol* may be related to this structural element. It first appears as the name for the early Anglo-Saxon man-of-war, whilst in the 10th century it is used to describe a type of cargo ship, and in modern English the sailing barges on the River Humber and the Tyne were called *keels*.

The keel's purpose was to give the ship a steady course when under way, to strengthen the hull longitudinally, to improve its sailing characteristics, and to protect the thin bottom planks from damage when landing on the shore. Thus is had to be of selected wood and could not be weakened by large treenail holes. Most of its length had preferably to be in a single piece, but there was no objection to the addition, forward and aft, of shorter or longer pieces

which provided a smooth transition to the stem and sternpost.

The shape of the stem and stern were almost alike, rising in a gentle curve from the keel and joining up with the sheerline (the top edge of the planking) to end in a point, a carved spiral, or less commonly, a dragon's head–'he had had a dragon's head made on the stem and stern of their ship'. *(Flatøy book.)* In the Oseberg ship a sufficient number of fragments of the upper part of the stem were found to make it possible to reconstruct it; the stem of the Gokstad ship was reconstructed conjecturally and it was not until the discovery of Skuldelev ship no.3 that a Viking ship with a fully preserved stem was found. This is a stem of V cross-section, with small 'steps' to which the strakes are clenched, in contrast to the stems of the *Gokstad* and

Oseberg ships which had rabbets into which the ends of the strakes were nailed.

Up to the present no Viking ship stem has been found of the type known only from rune stones and graffiti by its characteristic angular profile. Was the *Jernbarden* of Erik Jarl a ship like this? 'He had the ship which was called *Jernbarden* (Ironbeard); she was a big ship and exceedingly strong, both stem and stern were studded with much iron and with sharp spikes.' *(Fornmanna saga.)*

Keel sections, scale 1:20

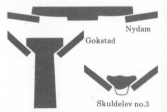

Nydam

Gokstad

Skuldelev no.3

The Bergen stick

To determine the measurements of the timber to be used for the keel, stem, sternpost and ribs the 18th century designers of naval vessels followed a series of rules. These rules were derived from hard-won experience. They proportioned components to the vessel's principal dimensions and the length of keel was the most important of these. The *Victory's* keel was 150 feet in length and this dictated its cross-section of 20 inches square. The depth of the keel beneath the upper edge of the *rabbet* (a deep groove or channel cut in it longitudinally, made to receive the edge of the lowest plank on the hull, known as the garboard strake), was half its depth.

Below the main keel was a *false-keel*, of four or five inches in thickness. This was of elm and secured with nails and copper staples which would give way and leave the main keel unscathed should the vessel strike the ground. The *Victory's* keel, originally of elm, was made up of several lengths of timber elaborately joined with scarfs and then bolted from above and below to give it the greatest degree of rigidity.

Above the keel the *floors* (the lowest section of the ribs) were laid. Above them the *keelson* was secured with bolts; the keelson, like the keel was built up from as many as five

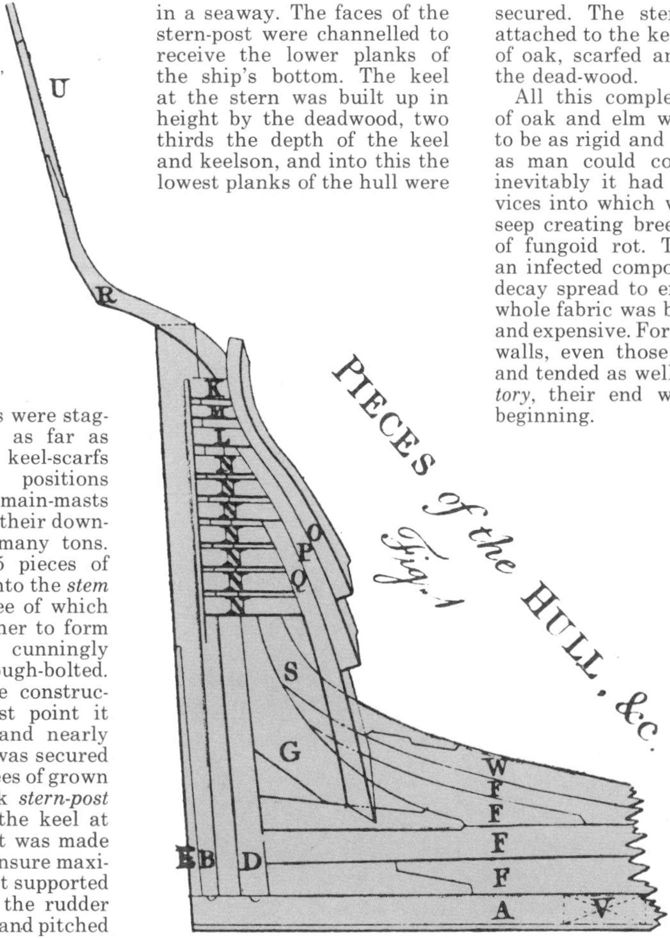

The stern post marked 'B' and its complex adjacent construction.

sections. The joints were staggered so they lay as far as possible from the keel-scarfs and avoided the positions where the fore and main-masts were stepped, with their downward pressure of many tons.

No less than 15 pieces of timber were built into the *stem* of the *Victory*, three of which were scarfed together to form the main member, cunningly jointed and through-bolted. The entire massive construction, at its deepest point it is ten feet thick and nearly two feet in width, was secured to the keel with knees of grown oak. The great oak *stern-post* was tenoned into the keel at the opposite end. It was made of a single tree to ensure maximum strength, for it supported the full weight of the rudder as the vessel rolled and pitched

in a seaway. The faces of the stern-post were channelled to receive the lower planks of the ship's bottom. The keel at the stern was built up in height by the deadwood, two thirds the depth of the keel and keelson, and into this the lowest planks of the hull were

secured. The stern-post was attached to the keel by a knee of oak, scarfed and bolted to the dead-wood.

All this complex structure of oak and elm was intended to be as rigid and long-lasting as man could contrive. But inevitably it had airless crevices into which water would seep creating breeding places of fungoid rot. To extricate an infected component before decay spread to endanger the whole fabric was both difficult and expensive. For the wooden-walls, even those as massive and tended as well as the *Victory*, their end was at their beginning.

PIECES of the HULL, &c.
Fig. 1

The ribs were fitted to the Viking ship at a late stage in her building, and had no effect in forming the shape of the hull. On the other hand they were very important for preventing the thin plank shell from breaking apart in the sea and when landing through surf. They were slender, springy ribs which could absorb hefty blows from waves and beaches and were sufficiently pliant to bend under the pressure. Twentieth century wooden lifeboats which run the risk of mighty impacts when being launched are also built with thin and pliant ribs.

In the Viking ships from the Norwegian graves the ribs are lashed to cleats which are left standing proud on the inboard side of the planks whilst these are being cut to shape. This technique of fixing the ribs in position has old traditions and it has undeniable advantages; first and foremost it dispenses with the necessity to bore treenail holes through the watertight plank shell to take the wooden pegs and, in addition, the lashings of natural fibre between the ribs and strakes help to give the ship her necessary elasticity. In Denmark, they adopted treenailed ribs as early as the 7th century AD, the ribs being fastened directly to the strakes with treenails fashioned from oak or willow. The earliest treenailed ribs retained the tradition of the oval cross section of the lashed rib, but later they become, as in the Skuldelev ships, of approximately rectangular cross-section varying in breadth like a long narrow 'bow-tie'. A significant advantage of treenailing was the saving of materials and labour with the disappearance of the cleats, but at the price of innumerable holes in the hull, each one a potential source of leakage and weakening the fabric. With the ship's movement at sea and when beaching, some of the treenails could work loose so that the water trickled in. Thus in the Skuldelev longship it was necessary to make several treenails tight by caulking them with sheep's wool. It is likely that the master shipwrights of the Gokstad and Oseberg ships with their sixteen oaken planks on each side, who cut out rib cleats long after others had begun to use treenails, felt themselves to be true master craftsmen building a vessel of the highest class in contrast to their treenail-cutting contemporaries who took the easy way out. But we must remember that the Oseberg ship was built for pleasure and not as a fighting unit.

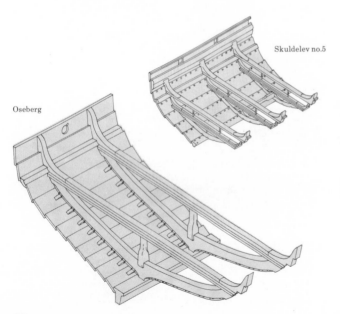

Skuldelev no.5

Oseberg

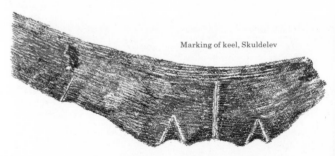

Marking of keel, Skuldelev

The ribs of the ship, which gave form to the hull, were known as *frames;* upon the outer faces the planking was fixed while on the inner faces the ceiling was nailed. In later times, these *frames* were pre-fabricated on the ground and then, suitably reinforced with temporary light fir planks so that their shape was retained, hoisted into position on the keel.

When the *Victory* was built frames were probably built up from *floor-timbers* which had first been placed transversely across the keel. These *floors,* or central section of the completed *frame,* were followed by the *dead-wood* aft and the filling and lower-transoms. The *keelson* was then run over the *floors* and was bolted into position. At this point a long piece of fir, some five inches square, was fixed to the outer ends of the *floors* and secured at the bow and stern. This enabled the shipwright to judge by eye if the shape was fair and the run of the floor was true. If all was to his satisfaction this ribband of fir was supported beneath with props from the ground.

To ensure that the *frames* were strong and long-lasting it was essential to select wood grown naturally to the correct curvature. This was referred to as *compass-timber.* It was the master shipwright's lot to be continually searching for

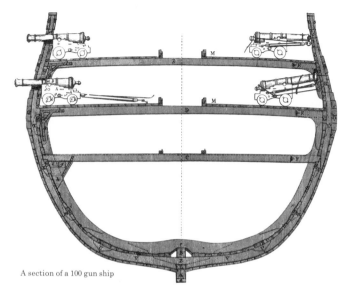

A section of a 100 gun ship

this essential material. To cut *frames* from inferior straight-grained wood was an ever-present temptation, but if it was done it could fatally reduce the strength of the hull. In later days shipwrights endeavoured to persuade designers to accept straighter-sided vessels so that *frames* would be less expensive to construct.

The *floors* were then extended on either extremity by the *frames,* beginning with the *first futtocks* (futtocks is a corruption of *foot-hooks*—

'hooks' being any curved piece of timber). Above the *first futtocks* were fixed the *second or ground futtocks,* above them the *third futtocks,* and finally the *top timbers.* These were jointed together and lifted into position. The construction of a strong joint was far from easy and various methods were used. *Chocks* were let into the ends of the futtocks and floors, and fixed with dowels; alternatively, scarfs were used, or a second rib might be added alongside, overlapping the joint and fitted to the first.

Upon the completion of the majority of the frames, special ones at the bow were fixed; these were called cant-timbers and like those at stern, known as *fashioned-pieces,* and were fixed at an angle to the dead wood aft and the apron forward. When the planking and the ceiling of the hull internally were completed, a three-decker had another series of frames built into her. These were less numerous than the main frames and originated with *floor-riders,* bolted into the keelson over the ceiling planks. With spaces provided either side, known as *limber holes,* there was provision for the ever-present bilge-water to reach the pumps.

The Admiralty had ordained that the *Victory* should be completed in 33 months; the more usual building time for a three-decker was five to ten years! Within little over a year the frames had risen, complete, on the keel; at this point it was usual for the whole complex framework to be allowed to settle and season. This period often dragged on for years and lime-wash was painted over the timbers to give some protection to the untreated wood. Lime-wash allowed the wood to breathe and to react to the weather, but it also prevented too violent a reaction to sudden changes in temperature of moisture content in the atmosphere.

Graffiti, Horbelev church

In the *Fornmanna saga* the story is told of the longship *Mariasuden* which King Sverre had built at Nidaros in 1182–83, at a time when no longships had been built in Norway for nearly 120 years. When he returned after being away for some time and found the ship planked up to the ninth strake, he had second thoughts, decided she was too small for him and ordered the ship to be cut in two amidships, and lengthened by 12 ells in spite of the master shipwright's protests. The king's order was carried out. Afterwards, the *Mariasuden* had many weak plank scarfs amidships, and towards the bow and stern her dimensions were too small.

'The *Mariasuden* was not a fair ship' says the saga honestly. When she was launched the scarfs gave way amidships and had to be repaired, and this happened again a year later in a storm. On that occasion the crew found out about the contents of four mysterious heavy chests which had previously been brought on board by four men. They were nails which were now distributed among the sailors with instructions to use them during the voyage wherever they were needed to repair the weakened hull made unsafe by the king ignoring his master-shipwright's advice.

This human story about the *Mariasuden* clearly illustrates the central problem of the ship-builders of the Viking and saga periods. When building ships which in principle were nothing more than long open boats, they had to strike a balance between the requirements of lightness and of strength. We do not know the length of the largest longships but the longship of the Skuldelev find measures about 28 metres in length. The difficulty lay first and foremost in the longitu-

dinal strength. With a length which is seven times her breadth the Ladby ship, like the Skuldelev warship, is exposed to strong forces produced when riding on one or two waves in a storm so that either the ends or the centre

section of the hull are left unsupported. Thus the Viking Age boatbuilders concentrated on two different parts of the structure to overcome this. First, they sought to prevent the upper strakes giving way amidships by nailing longitudinal reinforcements on some of them and by not having scarfs, always a point of weakness, in this area as far as

possible; thus the midship sections of the three upper ash strakes in the 18 metre long Skuldelev no. 5 ship are 10.0, 10.4 and 13.8 metres in length respectively. As a further safeguard the internal stability of the shell of the hull was ensured by the insertion of a cross beam and a thwart over each rib. Thus the sides of the ship could be prevented from bulging or collapsing when the waves tried to bend the ship along her length. In this way, paradoxically, the cross beams, securely fixed to ribs, contributed substantially to the longitudinal strength of the ship, and the ship as a whole attained the necessary combination of strength, elasticity and speed with a minimum weight of material.

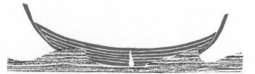

The heavy stern and bow construction of a wooden ship, the bow carrying the added burden of the bowsprit, were less well supported by water than the centre section and they tended to place a great strain on the keel and keelson. The gradual increase in the length of men-of-war which occurred during the 18th century had greatly accentuated this problem. This tendency for wooden vessels to drop at the bow and stern, and arch the hull, was called 'hogging'.

Although the great three-deckers, such as the *Victory*, suffered numerous endemic problems, hogging was not their most acute. The smaller frigates were another matter; their higher beam-length ratio and generally lighter construction made them susceptible to their ends dropping, particularly after service at sea for

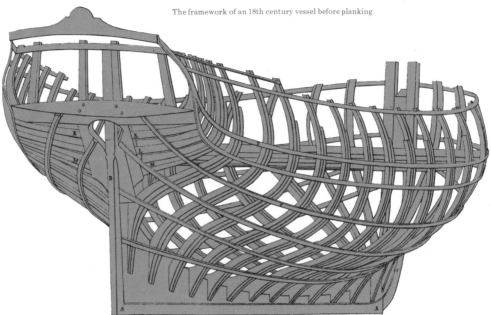

The framework of an 18th century vessel before planking

Types of scarfs

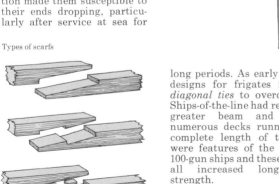

long periods. As early as 1768 designs for frigates indicate *diagonal ties* to overcome it. Ships-of-the-line had relatively greater beam and depth; numerous decks running the complete length of the hull were features of the 74- and 100-gun ships and these factors all increased longitudinal strength.

All ships, naval and merchantmen alike, were built with massive bands, or *wales*, of timber around the hull in an attempt to prevent hogging. On the *Victory* this was just above the waterline in the way of the lower-gun-deck. These *wales* were a belt of timber worked up from four layers of planks. Further precautions against *hogging* were made when planking-up. It was important that *butts*, the points at which the planks met

end-on, were staggered and all *butts* were to be separated vertically by at least three planks to avoid a line of weakness. The longer the individual planks were, the better, 24 feet being considered the safest minimum. The internal equivalent to *wales* were the *clamps* – they ran the length of the vessel under the deck-beams and also helped to strengthen the ship lengthwise.

In 1199, when King Sverre had taken some merchant ships in Nidaros for use as royal longships, he had them 'cut into pieces' so that their keels could be lengthened and that they could be fitted out to be 'rowed along the whole of the ship's side'. For it was especially the long continuous deck and the long line of oar ports which distinguished the warship from the merchant ship. In the warship the deck consisted of loose planks placed fore and aft in grooves in the sides of the cross beams. Forward and aft the deck was slightly raised. These were called *lok* or *stafnlok* forward and *lypting* aft. This could not be considered a deck in the modern sense; it was simply a raised floor to move about on, and it gave no shelter below from wind and weather. The origin of this planking deck is to be found in the thwarts of the Nydam boat, which developed into deck beams at a time when ships' sides were being heightened by fitting extra strakes. This stage is seen in the Oseberg ship, in which the former top strake now appears as a sturdy L-sectioned strake, the

meginhufr, on top of which have been added two planks supported by knees projecting from each *bite*, the former thwarts. When rowing, the crew of the Oseberg ship sat on moveable ship's chests, which were used to store the warrior's personal gear. Equipment could also be stored in the skin sleeping bag in the daytime and when coming on board and going ashore:–'he went on board then, he had a sleeping bag and a ship's chest' *(Sturlunga saga).*

In the Skuldelev warships the *meginhufr* has been inserted in line with the remaining strakes, and firm thwarts have been placed at each rib. Ribs, *biti* and thwarts with knees, preferably grown to shape, form a cross section which is important, even indispensable, in a long, low, narrow ship. In order to attain the desired lightness of structure the cross-beams were made as slender as possible–in the 5.2 metres broad Gokstad ship the *bite* measure about 17×6 cm; in the 2.5 metres broad Skuldelev warship the measurement of the *bite* is about 10×3 cm; whilst the thwarts were only 7–10 cm wide and 3.5 cm deep. These slender cross beams were supported in their centre by slim vertical pillars, named *snaelda*, because of their resemblance to the pointed spinning spindle of the Danes.

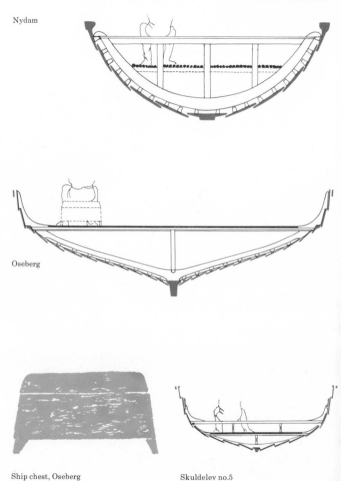

Nydam

Oseberg

Ship chest, Oseberg

Skuldelev no.5

The *Victory* was built with no fewer than four continuous decks; in addition, there were the *forecastle deck*, *quarter deck*, and *poop*, all of which gave shelter and space for guns and men. A ship-of-the-line of her strength had three fully-armed battery decks, the *upper*, *middle gun-deck*, and *lower-deck*. The original order for the *Victory* specified that the gun-ports of the lower-deck should be at least six feet above the water-line. In the past, men-of-war had been launched with their lowest gun-ports so dangerously close to the water-line that their use was extremely limited.

To support the immense weight of guns, each weighing at least two tons, and to sustain the strain of their recoil when fired, the decks were supported by great *beams*, at least one for each piece of ordnance, while those encompassing the mast were especially strengthened. In their turn the beams were secured fore and aft by *lodging knees* and beneath by *hanging knees*. These were amongst the first part of the wooden ship's fabric to be reinforced, and ultimately replaced, by iron—an innovation dating from at least 1769.

Over the beams the decks were laid, made from five-inch planks, caulked like the hull and sealed with pitch. The lowest deck of all, the *orlop deck*, was more lightly planked than the others. It was built below the water-line, but above the hold, and in its gloomy recesses were the cabins of the surgeon, carpenter, and boatswain. Here too was the grand magazine and the cockpit where the surgeon tended the wounded. From the orlop-deck ladders led down to the hold. Wooden pillars rose from the keelson at intervals amidst the ship's stores, to support the beams of the orlop-deck, and were carried upwards to give strength to those above, through to the upper-deck.

The upper-deck, unlike the others, was only covered by the forecastle forward and from the main mast aft by the quarter-deck, which contained the admiral's cabin. Amidship it was open to the sky. Although the beams above the upper-deck were uncovered it was a convenient place to stow the ship's boats and spare spars. Aft of the mizzen-mast and stretching to the taffrail, which carried the three huge lanterns, was the *poop-deck;* here the captain surveyed his kingdom. To reach the forecastle from aft it was not necessary to descend to the main deck with its guns, spars and where the carpenters were at work in the lee of the boats. Narrow platforms, called gang-ways, bridged the chasm to port and starboard, clear of the deck.

Gratings in the decks directly beneath one another gave a modest ventilation to those below and even less light. In heavy weather they were covered with tarpaulins, and such air and light as relieved the atmosphere below entered by way of the companion ways, one aft of the main mast and another forward. Under sail, in anything of a sea-way, water seeped in at the closed gun-ports and the hawse-holes forward; it penetrated the waterways and any ill-fitting fastenings wept. In the hold foul bilge-water washed back and forth across sour ballast. Small wonder that death from disease amongst the crew far exceeded many times the losses from enemy round-shot.

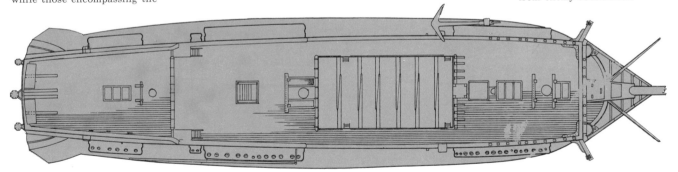

Carved stone, Stenkyrka

The idea of building to a modular system did not originate in modern times. As long as cattle were kept in the house, during the winter, the stable was built according to a 'cow module', and as long as vessels were propelled by oars, ships were built according to a 'rowing module', the space between the ribs, the *rum*. The space required by the oarsmen in terms of breadth, length and height is a decisive factor in the entire structure of the ship–the distance between the

ribs, the height of the deck, and the position of the thwarts and oar ports all depend on this. In the Viking ships and their predecessors each oarsman sat above a rib with his oar placed about halfway between that rib and the next. Thus the distance between the ribs is the main measurement of the 'rowing module' and is 90–100 cm in the Ladby ship and the Norwegian Viking ships. It looks as if, towards the end of the Viking period, there was an attempt to squeeze the oarsmen closer together so as to increase the number of sections without altering the length of the ship. The top strake in Skuldelev ship no.5 which has a distance between the ribs of 90 cm, previously belonged to another ship with a distance of 78 cm between the ribs, and the distance between the ribs in the longship Skuldelev no.2 is very short at 67–72 cm. In the longships the rowing positions were pre-determined so that each man knew his place. Right

aft there was a raised half deck, the *lypting* where the chieftain and the helmsman were, and where we can see them in many of the ships in the carved stones from Gotland. Forward of this was the *fyrirrum* where the chest with the weapons stood, and where the leaders were stationed during a fight on board. Then came a bailing station, the *austrrum;* and then the long midships portion, the *krapparum*, where the many oarsmen who made up the lower ranks of the crew worked the oars and the sails, and where moreover they lived day and night. The forepart of the ship also had its bailing station between the *krapparum* and the raised half deck, the *stafn*, forward in the bow. In some ships the *stafn* was supplemented by a space called the *sox* or *rausn*, and here the *stafnbuar*, the lookout man and the standard bearer or *merkismadr*, who lived in the bows, had their station.

The customs of reserving the

stern portion of the ship for the most distinguished persons on board is thus very old and it was not until the noisy propeller was fitted at this end of the ship that the practice ceased.

Rowing space Gokstad about 100 cm

Rowing Skuldelev no.5 about 92 cm

Rowing space Skuldelev no.2 about 70 cm

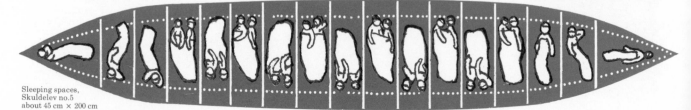

Sleeping spaces,
Skuldelev no.5
about 45 cm × 200 cm

The internal and external dimensions of the large warships of the 18th and early 19th centuries were determined by a module based upon the carriage-gun. On each gundeck of the *Victory* room had to be found for between 28 and 30 guns, evenly divided between port and starboard. The gun-module was dependent upon the size of the armament and the space needed to work it effectively, for they were all muzzle-loading. There was also the recoil of the gun and its wooden carriage to be considered and the space needed for the bringing up of the black-powder charges from the magazine below, always a potential source of danger

The sailors' mess between the guns

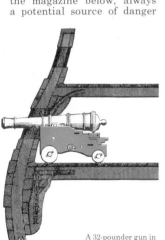

A 32-pounder gun in firing position

and accommodation for the round-shot. Each iron gun on the crowded 'tween-decks of the *Victory* needed at least ten feet between adjacent pieces. This was the ultimate determinant of the size of a man-of-war; the accommodation of the men was a secondary consideration to that of the armament. The crew slept, ate, and found such recreation as a constricted life provided, in the narrow space between the guns they served in battle. At sea the guns were lashed to ringbolts so that they would not break adrift.

It was important that the guns should discharge their shot, as far as possible, from a steady platform. If the inevitable movement of the ship at sea could be reduced, or

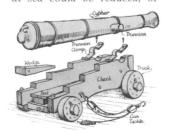

was at least predictable, it gave a greater chance to the master gunner to silence the enemy, particularly in a chase. A wide beam helped and the correct positioning of the greatest width of the hull in relationship to the overall length and depth was important.

Calculation of the tonnage depended upon the ratio of length to beam. But there was a very limited understanding of the fundamental ways in which a sea-kindly hull might be produced in the century which saw the launch of the *Victory*.

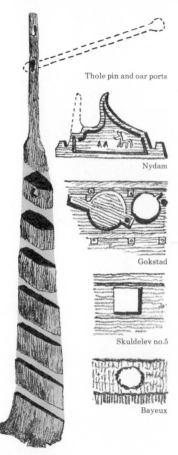

Thole pin and oar ports

Nydam

Gokstad

Skuldelev no.5

Bayeux

Side rudder, Vorså

Unlike the galley-slaves of the Mediterranean the oarsmen of the Viking ship were freemen, warriors and sailors who pulled on the oars without any slaver's whip over their backs. Normally there was one man to each oar, but the Sagas tell us that when there was sufficient crew on board the King's ship, up to four men could pull on each oar so that the ship flew along like a bird over the waves.

The length of the oar was suited to the height of the oar ports above the water, so that the oar was properly balanced. In the Gokstad ship the midship oar ports are 48 cm above the water-line (towards the ends they are slightly higher), whilst the oars are 12 times as long as this, ie, 5.30 to 5.85 metres. The oars were put out through ports in the ship's side. In the Gokstad ship these ports are cut in the third strake from the sheer, and could be closed by small wooden discs; in other Viking ships they are in the top strake. They are square or round with a notch, and of such a size that the oar blade can just be passed through.

Ships of the Viking age were steered by a side rudder, a broad oar which was fastened well aft on the starboard side, the *stjornbordi* (or occasionally on the port side, the *bakbordi* as is indicated in

some finds). The rudder was turned about its longitudinal axis by means of a tiller. A withy held the rudder against a boss on the ship's side. When sailing in deep water, the rudder extended down below the keel, but on running in to shallow coastal waters the rudder was rotated in its mounting, the stock being turned forward and downward and the blade backwards and upwards. A side rudder recovered in 1958 from the Kattegat outside Vorså shows how carefully its construction had been thought out: we see that the tiller has two holes for use in the rudder's two positions. The cross-section of the rudder blade is like the wing of a bird, and when the ship is under way this exerts a sideways thrust on the hull aft which automatically compensates for the water resistance of the rudder, so that the ship of her own accord keeps on a straight course.

In 1893 the Norwegians built a full-size replica of the Gokstad ship and sailed her across the Atlantic. The captain, Magnus Andersen, trusted the ship but not the side rudder, so he took a spare rudder with him to be mounted at the sternpost if necessary. It was not necessary 'for the side rudder is wonderful and, after the experience I now have, I find it greatly to be preferred to a rudder on the sternpost for a ship like this.'

The propulsion of the conflicting battle fleets of the 18th century was almost entirely dependent upon sail. A complex system of masts, spars and canvas had slowly evolved from the primitive square-sail of the Vikings to drive the immensely heavier hulls of the men-of-war with their batteries of guns. The pace of change in the rig of sea-going ships had greatly accelerated during the second half of the 15th century. The adoption of a sail normally carried in a fore and aft line, called a lateen sail and set on the aftermost mast was matched by the introduction of a square-sail beneath the bowsprit forward. Large vessels carried three or more masts and this produced, together with the other innovations, the ocean-going, sea-keeping ship. Moreover, artillery could now be used afloat with success.

The triangular lateen sail was secured to a long, tapering yard. By the mid-18th century it had lost the canvas carried forward of the mast, although the long yard survived. When the *Victory* was launched she carried a yard of this type, although later it was discarded in favour of a *gaff*. This spar carried the *driver* which assisted in steering and manoeuvring the ship.

The adoption of a rudder hinged on the sternpost anticipated the introduction of other developments by several centuries. As soon as the stern rudder was accepted as more effective on bigger ships than its predecessor the side rudder, the old hull-form of the Viking was doomed. The hinged rudder required a straight sternpost and accommodation for the helmsman. The *Victory's* great rudder hung on the sternpost by at least seven wrought-iron gudgeons and pintles. The rudder was chamfered throughout its whole inner edge so that it might be turned without fouling the sternpost. Turning the rudder was effected by the tiller, a long bar of timber, morticed into the rudder-head. This led inboard through the tiller-hole, which was protected by canvas cloaks, and its movement controlled by tiller ropes, connecting through blocks to the ships wheel. Five turns of the tiller-rope were usually wound round the barrel of the wheel. The maximum amount of movement that could be transmitted by the helmsman to the rudder was limited, but a sailing-ship, unlike a power-driven vessel, does not normally require sudden or extreme alterations of direction unless they are accompanied by sail-trimming, which assists the efforts of the helmsman.

The *Victory's* steering-wheel was under the supervision of the chief quartermaster and was operated by four men in moderate weather, but this number was doubled in deteriorating conditions of wind and sea. In the event of damage to the wheel the ship was steered by men hauling on tackles attached to the tiller on the lower gun-deck.

The sail plan of a ship-of-the-line

1. Fore royal
2. Main royal
3. Mizzen royal
4. Main royal staysail
d. Main course or Main sail
e. Main topsail
f. Main topgallant sail
g. Fore course or Foresail
h. Fore topsail
i. Fore topgallant sail
k. The driver
l. Mizzen topsail
m. Mizzen topgallant
o. Mainmast staysail
p. Main topmast staysail
q. Main topgallant staysail
r. Mizzen staysail
s. Mizzen topmast staysail
t. Fore topmast staysail
u. Jib
y. Spritsail

The pride of the Viking ship was the single squaresail which was so important that Sigurd Jorsalafarer, on his voyage to the Holy Land, had his ship wait half a month off the Greek coast, in spite of his having a very fair wind for continuing his voyage along the coast, so that he could use a cross wind which would display his fine sail at the best angle! But *his* sail was covered with the finest silk on both sides for, according to the saga, none of the crew, whether their place was forward or aft, wanted to look on a less fine part of the sail. It is remarkable that mast and sail do not appear in Scandinavian waters until a few centuries before the Viking period. For thousands of years they paddled their boats; for hundreds of years they rowed; and then, finally they learnt to fit the mast into the hull and to sail. They probably found their teachers in western Europe where sailing techniques had been known from before the time of the Roman conquest.

It was something of a problem to fit the mast into the slender clinker-built hull of the Norse ship. There was a great force from the pressure of the wind on the sail and downwards from the weight of the mast and yard which had to be transferred to the mast step in the keelson or 'kerling' (from which comes French *carlingue*, English *carling*), a heavy block of wood resting on the upper surface of the keel and covering the central ribs. In the Oseberg ship the keelson extends over two ribs, in the Gokstad ship over four and in the longship from the Skuldelev find over 19 ribs. This distributed the weight of the mast over as large an area as possible.

Keelson, Skuldelev

In the Norse Viking ship the mast is supported at the height of the bottom boards by a 'mast fish' or 'mast partner' a heavy piece of timber with a longitudinal slot which helped to control the mast when it was being lowered. A considerable part of

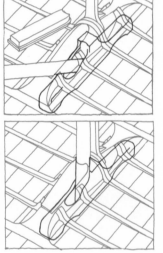

How the mast is raised, Gokstad

the pressure from the mast has to be borne by this mast fish; the slender mast fish in the Oseberg ship had split and had been repaired with strips of iron. The mast fish in the Gokstad ship is in the shape of a fish tail at the ends but this is not, as one might believe, the reason for the name. In Old Norse the part was called *klofi* (=cleft) because of its divided form.

Merchant ships did not have a mast fish, but a heavy mast beam against which the mast rested. Masts in merchant ships remained stepped in the hull from the time the ship

was launched in the spring until the sailing season was over, but aboard warships the mast was often unstepped. This was usually done without difficulty, but on one occasion there was a mishap:–'they were to step the mast on the royal ship, but when the mast was raised, it fell forward against the 'sticks' (gallows bitts) in the forepart of the ship, but this was due to there being ice in the mast step'. (*Fornmanna saga*).

28

Amongst the artisans of the royal dockyards the mast-makers held a position of especial honour. Their task would have been straightforward if they had been able to purchase timber so large that the various masts of a man-of-war could have been shaped from a single tree. But timber of the required dimensions for this was not available. This was partly over-come by each mast being divided into three sections. The *lower-mast*, whose heel was stepped on the keelson, was joined to the *top-mast*, while above this came the *topgallant mast*, terminated by the truck. Where the lower-mast held the heel of the top-mast was a platform called the 'top' and the topgallant mast was secured to the head of the top-mast by wooden crosstrees.

But even this three-fold division did not solve the mast-makers' problems. The total height of the *Victory's* main-mast, from keelson to truck, was some 240 feet, with a maximum girth of 7½ feet, tapering to 18 inches at the truck. To achieve this diameter the mast-makers were forced to assemble a mast from 12 or more long pine trunks which were sawn and adzed into an ingenious inter-locking system so that it became a single rigid spar, held together by rope-woldings. These were replaced by iron hoops by about 1800.

The supplies of large masts' timbers for Europe's men-of-war came partly from the Baltic and partly from North America. During the American War of Independence, when the British fleet could not import American masts, there was, for a few years, a catastrophic situation for the men-of-war. With masts needing replacements which could not be found, disasters occurred such as the dismasting of the 74-gun *Invincible* in 1778 which lost first her mainmast and then her foremast when on duty in the Atlantic. Lighter spars and masts were carried on board which could be given their final shaping by the carpenter and his assistants and then sent aloft to replace damage sustained by weather or the king's enemies.

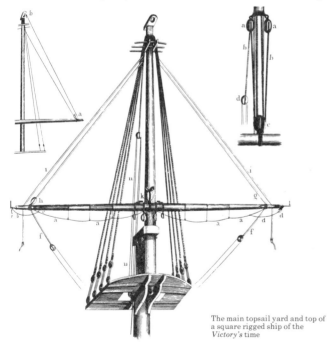

The main topsail yard and top of a square rigged ship of the *Victory's* time

The mast of a ship-of-the-line with its standing rigging

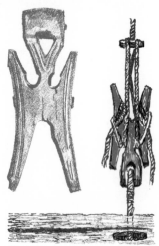

'Virgin' block

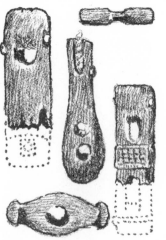

Blocks

When the buried Gokstad ship was discovered, the upper part of the stem and stern and the top strake amidships were broken or rotted away, so that all traces of the shrouds and stays supporting the mast had disappeared – or so it was thought. However, inside the ship there were various parts of the rigging, including four strange pieces of carved wood almost in the shape of a female human figure with arms, legs and head. For a long time the purpose of these was not understood until an acute person realised that they were used to tauten or 'set-up', the

shrouds. The unusual shape has its origin in the 'growing together' of two cleats around an eye. With a thin rope fastened to either side of this block the shrouds could conveniently be tightened as necessary, or easily slackened right off when the mast had to be unstepped. The present English name for this element is 'deadeye', but the name in the Scandinavian languages, *jomfru* (=virgin) is explained by the shape of the Gokstad specimen.

There were usually two, three or four shrouds on either side, sometimes supplemented by an extra pair which could be moved from one side to the other and thus support the tall pine mast and its sail on the windward side. The mast, some 10 metres in height, was also supported forward by a

Seal, Sandwich

stay, and the halyard (*dragreip*), with which the yard of the sail was hoisted, could be made fast on the ship's side aft to serve as a back-stay, important when the vessel was running before the wind. During the excavation of the Skuldelev small merchant ship, remains were found of two rings of twisted willow by which the shrouds had been fastened to the top strake on either side of the mast. This might seem more primitive than it actually is, for a willow ring is a good hard-wearing expedient in such an exposed position. Shrouds and stays in this small merchant ship were

presumably of rope spun from lime bast or possibly from hemp which, we know from archaeological evidence, has been used in Scandinavia since the Viking period, perhaps imported as seed by the Vikings after a voyage down the rivers of Russia to the Near East. In other cases they provided themselves with the strongest and toughest rope one could get, *svardreip*, which was the skin of the walrus or seal, spirally cut from the snout to the tip of the tail. This much sought-after *svardreip* was one of the most important exports from the Norse colonies in Greenland.

The rigging of a sailing man-of-war was the product of lessons learnt from the severest testing that battle and storm could devise. Success in battle went to the vessels with the most effective rigging and the survival of a ship at sea depended upon the seaman-like use of sails, spars and rope. Evolution of equipment was slow because materials were limited and the penalty demanded by the sea for an unsuccessful experiment was heavy.

For ships-of-the-line, frigates and sloops, the rigging plan was identical except in scale and for minor details. They were all *fully-rigged* (setting some 37 individual sails) with three masts known as the *foremast*, *mainmast*, and *mizzen*. Each mast carried four yards. The heaviest, the *main-yard*, was slung from heavy rope slings; above it came the *topsail yard*, then the *topgallant* and finally the *royal*. This was

Blocks

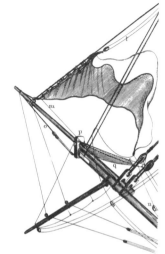

The bowsprit and jib boom

the highest of the four and was frequently stowed on deck and only sent aloft when required.

The *masts* and the *bowsprit* had their lower ends secured in a block below decks and were to a certain extent secured by deck-beams. However, their support was derived mainly from the *standing-rigging*, spun from hemp, tarred and as thick as a man's leg. *Shrouds* led from the mast's top to the side of the ship while *back-stays* gave support to the upper masts and were balanced by *stays* which led

forward. They were all blacked with Stockholm tar in an attempt to render them rot-proof.

For the trimming of the sails on their yards and their control a complicated net-work of ropes, known collectively as the *running-rigging*, was used. On the *Victory* the mainsail contained some 500 square yards of canvas, slung from a main-yard 100 feet in length. There were over ten thousand yards of rope and cordage in the *Victory's* rigging and more than one thousand wooden pulleys and blocks.

The rigging, with all its complexities and vulnerability to wear and damage, was the responsibility of the boatswain whose badge of authority was his silver whistle and its thin silver chain. He and his mates were expected to inspect every inch of rigging daily. The boatswain was also responsible for the trim of the ship, its anchors, cables and flags and before going into action it was his duty to see that chains and tackles for repairing rigging were in their place.

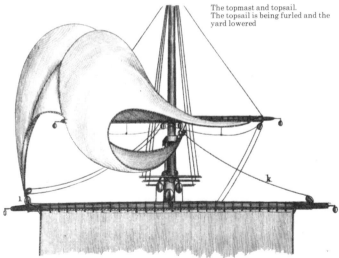

The topmast and topsail.
The topsail is being furled and the yard lowered

over the stem as a bowsprit. This boom could be fixed in a block on either side before the mast, similar to the 20th century *vargord* or spar used in Cornish dipping lug-rigged fishing boats. When the sail area was to be reduced, they slackened off the halyard so that the yard with the sail slid down a little for reefing.

In the expertly executed series of pictures in the Bayeux Tapestry we find, time and time again, scenes which, in an amusing and striking fashion, characterise a situation as well as, or better than, the best comic strip of today. We see this in the scene in which the English earl Harold Godwinson embarks with his entourage during a hunting expedition and is driven off his course by a storm so that he is forced to land in Normandy. In the section of the scene reproduced

here we see the company wading out to their ship with their stockings off and their hunting dogs and falcons in their arms; we see the ship being pushed off and rowed away from the land, the anchor being weighed and the mast stepped. In the next picture, we see the ship under way with shields along the gunwale and the ship's boat in tow, whilst the helmsman gives his orders. The bow of the ship is already coming into such shallow water that the man in the bows must take soundings of the depth with a pole. This whole scene is an excellent supplement to the descriptions of ship operations in the sagas and the conclusions one can draw from other illustrations and finds.

It looks as if the Norse sailors had teething troubles in keeping control of the sails before the sail attained its definitive design in the Saga period. We can see from stone scribings that the sail of an eighth century longship has a complete network of ropes

along its lower edge and that each man is holding the sail taut with a rope's end. This system has been variously interpreted as being extra sheets, or as 'Venetian blind strings' with which the sail is reefed. On some of the other carved stones from Gotland a less complicated system is shown, but the variations in the system of ropes and in the structure of the diamond-patterned sail, which in some illustrations has a serrated bottom edge, cannot yet be satisfactorily explained. During the Viking period the rigging was simplified so that the sail, which was seized to the yard with bands, could be operated solely by means of sheets which passed aft from the lower corners of the sail and tacks forward from the same corner; sometimes, perhaps with the addition of braces fastened to the outer extremities of the yard. When sailing close to the wind the foremost edge of the sail, or luff, was held taut by a bowline, or by a special tacking boom

Running with
bearing out spars

Reaching with
tacking boom

Ship-of-the-line *London* under
plain sail before the wind

The square-sail, made from flax set on a yard slung from the mast, continued to be the primary form of propulsion for the whole of the sailing ship era for a wide range of European vessels. The single sail of the Viking ship persisted until well into the Middle Ages but about the middle of the 15th century the largest ships began to be fitted with two or three masts, and a little later a fore and aft sail became usual on the after-most mast. Early in the 18th century gaff and staysails came into general use and the whole arrangement of canvas on an 18th century ship-of-the-line reflected an international tradition developed through the centuries. It represented the most efficient use of the limited raw materials available and had the great advantage of being easily repaired and adaptable. But it required a great expenditure of muscle power to control it and an innate conservatism tended to delay innovation in rigging and sail plans.

The crew required to work and fight the *Victory* numbered nearly one thousand. At sea there were always some 250 men immediately on call to tend the sails. Mature seamen, some 60 to 70 in number, who knew their duty well, were stationed on the forecastle to handle the anchors, head-sails and the fore-yard, essential in manoeuvring the ship. Next were the topmen, one division for each mast, fore, main (some 40 or 70 men each) and for the mizzen which needed fewer, some 25 or 30 who were frequently the less experienced members of the crew. They handled the sails above the main yard, particularly the demanding task of reefing the topsails. The task of furling the sails was lightened with the help of clew-lines and bunt-lines, hauled upon by the less skilled seamen who worked on deck and were known as the after-guard. This group also worked the driver, main-sail and lower stay-sails. All, when they went aloft, used the ladder-like ratlines on the shrouds and when out on the yards, stood in the footropes which were suspended under the yard.

Triangular headsails, called jibs, were only regularly fitted to large men-of-war 30 or 40 years before the launch of the *Victory* and were set in conjunction with the much older *spritsail*, the name given to the square sail carried under the bowsprit. The jibs and the similar sails set on the rope stays between the masts did much to improve the sailing qualities of the men-of-war, enabling them to beat windward with greater ease.

When running before the wind the effective area of canvas of a man-of-war was reduced to little more than the square sails set on one mast. To overcome this, *studding-sails* were used on the extremities of the lower yards; narrow squaresails temporarily set on booms which were, in effect extensions to the yards. They were carried on the main, top and topgallant yards of the main and foremast. To set and trim them required a highly trained division of topmen and a skilled quartermaster at the ship's helm.

Under sail on the port tack

'For these men, shipwreck is an everyday occurrence and not something which fills them with terror. The dangers of the deep are for them not occasional acquaintances but close friends.' This is how Sidonius, a nobleman from 5th century Roman Gaul describes the Anglo-Saxon voyagers who were crossing the sea and settling on the eastern shores of England.

It was the same seamanship which made the Vikings known and feared. Their vessels have been called the last really seaworthy ocean-going landing craft in the history of the world. In the Skuldelev warships the worn underside of the keel and the bottom boards bear clear witness to the fact that these ships have been beached upon rough,

boulder-strewn shores countless times. Where other vessels would be wrecked, they could approach an open coast, sail the ship through the surf without damage or loss to either ship or crew. This difficult technique is familiar to the west coast fishermen in the fishing villages of North Jutland where to this day they land on the open coast. Here, the art of manoeuvring a boat in the surf is practised from childhood. The rescue of many a shipwrecked person on the west coast of Jutland is due to the life-boat crew's having mastered this hereditary art. Whenever possible, the Vikings followed the coastline, and landed or anchored for the night. On William the Conqueror's channel crossing in 1066, his large fleet of ships followed the lantern on top of William's ship, the *Mora*, through the hours of darkness. Navigation was a problem for these early voyagers when they sailed out of sight of land. The compass was not known to them and neither, naturally,

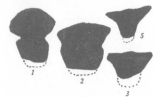

Wear of the keels of the Skuldelev ships

were the sextant or chronometer. Nevertheless, they were capable of such exacting ocean navigation as the successful crossing of the Atlantic to Iceland and Greenland. As long as the sky remained clear, they could navigate by latitude. This was done by measuring the height of the pole star (*leidarstjarna*) or of the sun, above the horizon; and in overcast weather they could try to find the direction of the sun with their *solarsteinn*, a piece of double-refracting Iceland felspar.

One of the most important parts of the ship's equipment was the anchor and cable. It could be of wood weighted with stone (*stjori*) or of iron with a wooden stock (*akkeri*). In the Ladby ship the anchor was found to be preserved and it

was in the shape of a present-day anchor but with smaller flukes. The anchor weighed only 40–50 kg. but it was fitted with a length of iron chain between the anchor and the anchor rope. This arrangement ensured a good hold on the sea-bed, since the iron chain could take up the pull of the ship and prevent the anchor rope being worn on the stones of the sea-bed. Useful though the iron chain was for this purpose, it was given up or forgotten in the Middle Ages and not used again until the beginning of the 19th century.

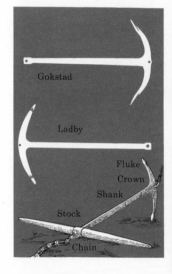

The main capstan of a naval vessel could be manned at main and upper deck level

When the *Victory* was at sea it was the duty of the master to see that she proceeded about the king's business with safety and expedition. He was next in rank to the first lieutenant and his duties related to all that concerned the movement of the ship. Every day at noon the ship's position was calculated by dead reckoning (an assessment of distance and direction sailed) and also by quadrant. In foreign waters he was responsible for surveying inshore, checking his charts, and if one was not available, make one. Masters could improve their pay by qualifying as pilots for home and foreign ports.

At noon he shared the poop of the *Victory* with the officer of the day and with his quartermaster and a group of midshipmen under instruction, took sights with quadrants in order to determine the ship's position. He checked the logbooks of his assistants in which was recorded a full account of the ship's movements and the calculations relating to its course.

The master's duty was not restricted to this but extended to the trimming and set of the sails, in battle and when on passage or patrol. Often it was his skill that extricated the unhandy ships-of-the-line from a lee-shore, or enabled a battered veteran to ride out a gale. The more mundane duties of stowing ballast, stores and equipment in the hold were his and also the care of the cable-tier. The cable-tier was a section of the orlop-deck devoted to the ship's cable and where it was coiled and stowed away, under the supervision of the bosun. Cables and anchors were of prime importance to the safety of the ship, while anchor-work had an importance in the manoeuvring of a sailing-ship which we tend to forget. The cables were fully 25 inches in circumference and made from hemp. Ships-of-the-line did not expect to anchor in water much deeper than 40 fathoms (240 feet), but at least twice this length of cable was needed to ensure a ship rode easily. There were two *sheet anchors* aboard a well-equipped ship, each weighing four tons, two *bower anchors*, besides the smaller *stream* and *kedge anchors*. When the cable was run out its speed was controlled by two iron *cable-compressors* forward. These were operated by tackles, so as to grip and arrest the cables run through the hawse-hole at the bow.

The recovery of the cable was done by an endless 11-inch rope, known as a *messenger*. It was the messenger and not the cable that was taken round the great capstan and it was secured to the cable itself by short lengths of rope. These were progressively made fast and then cast off from the cable as the great dripping monster

came inboard through the hawse-hole. It was possible to man the capstans with as many as 280 seamen, ten men at each bar, tramping round. Once the anchor was clear of the water it was hauled up by purchases to the cat-heads, projecting wooden beams on the forecastle head, and then securely lashed to prevent chafe to the hull.

The great anchor hanging from the cathead

For as long as ships have been built they have been decorated with painting, carving and symbolic decoration. In all ages and over the whole world it has been the practice to put an emblem, usually a head human or animal, in the bow. Customs with very ancient roots have been followed without it always being known where they originated, but with the figurehead it was simple for seamen to find an explanation: the two eyes could guide the ship on a straight course and prevent them from losing their sense of direction at sea, whilst, at the same time, the gaping mouth of a dragon could give any enemies who came along an initial and very useful fright. Time and time again the sagas tell of the dragon heads of large ships. King Håkon's long ship, the *Maria-sud*, is described as a *dreki* (dragon ship) with gold-orna-mented figureheads in the stems, and this can scarcely have been unusual. Dragon ships were always *hofudskip* (ships with figureheads), prob-ably also the *skeidir* had dra-gon heads, and often also the larger *kaupskip* (merchant ships). These fearsome, painted figureheads were detachable . and the wedges with which

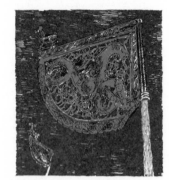

Weather vane

they were made fast can be seen in many illustrations. In special cases the stem might be decorated with something other than a dragon head, for example, on William the Con-queror's ship of 1066 there is a horn-blower aft as a deco-ration and an emblem. It is obvious that they wanted to distinguish some of the ships by hanging shields with easily recognisable emblems on the stems. But the majority of the ships in the fleet would be unlikely to have had any spe-cial stem decoration.

At the top of the mast or the stem there might be a weather-vane, a bronze plate of fine design to which were sewn bunting or coloured rib-bons. Some of these weather vanes from the Viking period are preserved to this day on top of church towers, having for centuries shown the direc-tion of the wind by their dra-gonlike shape.

The planks of a newly-built ship were usually tarred and the tarring renewed each autumn, but now and then the pleasures of colour were admit-ted, as the ship's name *Redside* (*Raudsida*) indicates. Each

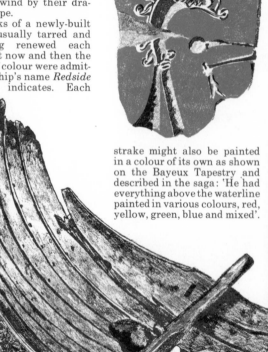

strake might also be painted in a colour of its own as shown on the Bayeux Tapestry and described in the saga: 'He had everything above the waterline painted in various colours, red, yellow, green, blue and mixed'.

The *Victory*, as a ship-of-the-line of the mid-18th century, carried a relatively restrained amount of decoration compared with its counter-part of the 17th century. Carved ornamentation was largely restricted to the bow and stern. When she was launched the *Victory* was embellished at the bow with a complicated 'group' figurehead, typical of the period, no less than 24 feet long and 18 feet broad and involving over a dozen figures. It was created by William Savage of Chatham and a carver's model of it is in the National Maritime Museum. The Admiralty issued an order in 1796 restricting still further the carved decoration on ships and perhaps because of this, when the *Victory* underwent a large refit in 1802 and the figurehead was found to be rotten, it was replaced by a much simpler device. This was renewed in turn by the one borne by the *Victory* today, which it resembles, and consists of an emblazoned badge with two supporters.

It was usual to associate the vessel's name with the design of its figurehead, although until the 18th century many of the royal ships carried a rampant lion, touched out and with a gold crown. When the *Horatio* was launched in 1804, a Fifth-Rate, she carried a carving of Nelson, vigorously done and showing his right eye closed.

The wide stern of the *Victory* borrowed its design and detailing from the patterns of classical architecture ashore. When she was launched it consisted of two elaborate, gilded open galleries above her name which was emblazoned across the transom, above the rudder entry, with a great deal of 'ginger-bread' work. The stern galleries merged with a three-tier range of quarter-galleries which lit the officers' cabins. After the rebuilding of 1802 the galleries, favourite places for the captain and his entourage to take the air, were enclosed for they were very vulnerable to enemy gun fire. The decoration became rather more restrained and the name board much shorter.

When the *Victory* was launched there was no uniformity of colour scheme for men-of-war. Captains of ships were left to their own devices, restricted only by the cost of paint and the resources of the dockyard. But below the water-line men-of-war were uniformly painted white; copper sheathing did not become accepted until later. Above the water-line on the *Victory* came a broad band of black, above this she wore a dull yellow tinge, occasioned by coats of varnish; only later did the space between the tiers of guns acquire a band of black. Blue, scarlet and touches of gilt relieved the upper works while

The stern of the First-Rate HMS *Prince*

white and gold were considered appropriate for the upper-deck. The masts, like the sides of the ship, were yellow with varnish (for paint might well hide defects in the timber), set off by black iron bands and black spars.

Below the upper-deck the officers' cabins were panelled and one colour only was employed on the gun-decks—scarlet. It was traditionally said to have been introduced by Admiral Robert Blake to

disguise the effects of the carnage of battle. More prosaically the red-lead must have provided the timber work with an excellent preservative. The port-lids, or gun-port shutters, were, of course, also painted on their inner sides in red. When the lids were raised for the guns to be fired, by ropes which were fitted to their lower run and drawn inboard through leaden pipes, the vessel's sides were enlivened with scarlet patches.

In 826, when Ansgar and the Danish King, Harald Klak, received as a gift from the Archbishop of Cologne 'an excellent ship' with two cabins, for their voyage home to Denmark, they were brought face to face with a luxury to which no hardy Scandinavian seafarer of the period was accustomed. The Scandinavian ships were in principle open boats without any weather deck, and life on board was spent round the clock in the open by everyone from the captain to the oarsmen and the cook. They had to find room for themselves and their gear in the narrow space between thwarts, mast and ship's sides. As far as possible they anchored at night in a natural harbour or in the lee of a conveniently situated island where they could pitch their tent either on land or on board. The tent cloth was erected on a frame consisting of a pole resting at either end on a pair of crossed boards. On the king's ship the *lyptingartjald*, the tent in the stern, was reserved for the king and his immediate entourage.

The light construction of the traditional Viking ships and their frequent beaching meant that they were far from watertight after a season's voyaging. Skuldelev ship no. 2 had given at the joints so much during the vessel's movements in the sea that the treenails had widened their holes and made the bottom leaky. There was thus good reason for bailing with a scoop. It was something of a problem to keep the slimly built ships watertight without a pump and thus the Gulating law lays down: 'If one man can keep the water out on

a long voyage (actually on a main route) by bailing, the ship is quite seaworthy'.

Even if they could keep dry with the help of the tent and by means of bailing, it can scarcely have been a pleasure to sleep on board a warship or stand watch on a bitterly cold autumn night. They might have kept tolerably warm by creeping into the double sleeping bag which was made of skins sewn together in the form of a large sack to hold two men who were then known as *hudfatsfelagar* or sleeping sack companions. Beds were not used on board. The finely carved bed from the Oseberg ship is a part of the funeral trappings, as are the sleighs and carriages which were also brought on board for the burial.

The cook did not become a specific person on board until the 11th century, and a galley was unknown. If warm food was to be prepared it had to be done ashore where the large iron or copper pot was used to cook porridge over a fire. At sea they had to make do with cold food, dried halibut or dried codfish, with water or ale from the tub. If their stores were used up, they had, in certain circumstances, the right to provision themselves ashore, to have a 'shore harvest'. At times several sailors had provisions in common and were called *motunautar* from which comes the Old French *matenot*, and modern French *matelot*, and Danish *matros*.

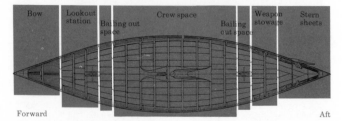

Forward

Aft

Life on board a ship-of-the-line was a harsh affair for everyone on the lower deck and might be highly disagreable for even the senior officers. Even if judged by the standards of the 18th century the seamen lived a brutish existence, poorly fed and worse used.

The crew were divided into two watches, and each worked for spells of four hours apiece, except between the hours of four o'clock in the afternoon and eight o'clock in the evening. This period was divided into 'dog-watches' of two hours, so that the routine might daily alternate. In times of stress the shout of 'all hands on deck' brought the watch below tumbling from their hammocks to deal together with those on duty, with any emergency.

The ships day began at 4 am. with the cook lighting the galley fire and the carpenter and his mates commencing their duties. Those on duty scrubbed down the decks, sanding them and scouring them with holystones and at half past seven 'All-hands, up hammocks' was piped by the boatswain. The canvas hammocks, which were slung from hooks between the guns on the lower and middle deck while the crew slept, were lashed-up and stowed in wooden troughs surmounting the ship's bulwarks. They were covered with tarred or painted canvas to give them

At anchor in Gravesend Reach at the end of a long commission the seamen relax

some protection from the elements and in the event of an engagement offered a breakwork against small-arms' fire. Where the men had slept, with scarcely an inch between them, the mess tables were lowered into position and breakfast, usually *burgoo*, an oatmeal gruel, was issued from huge coppers. It was washed down with 'Scotch coffee', produced from burnt and browned biscuit, ground and added to boiling water.

It was then the turn of the lower decks to be cleaned, carried out by the watch below, with an occasional sponging-down with vinegar as a gesture towards disinfection.

Then the guns were exercised and at six bells, or 11 o'clock, the captain came on deck with his black list of wrong doers. With the crew

mustered the master-at-arms, the chief of the ship's police, presented the prisoners due for punishment with the cat-o'-nine-tails. Three dozen strokes on the bare back were a common chastisement, and three hundred were not unknown. While this savage punishment was administered the marines in scarlet uniform, with their muskets and side-arms fell in on the poop to quell any who might be reckless enough to obstruct the due processes of naval law. There were humane captains who rarely resorted to these accepted methods of maintaining authority, but they were always in a minority.

At twelve the seamen ate dinner. It was taken in groups of from four to eight seamen, one of whom collected a communal ration from the galley. Boiled salt pork and duff, only

rarely flavoured with raisins and currants, alternated with coarse, salt beef, unsweetened biscuit baked from mixed wheat and pea flour, not uncommonly adulterated with bone meal. Sometimes cheese, which bred long, red worms, was issued from the depths of the purser's store.

Noon also saw the issuing of beer, (water soon became undrinkable stored in wooden casks) and when this was exhausted, wine or 'grog', a mixture of one gill of rum and three gills of water, was substituted. For the seamen this was the pleasantest part of the day. Then the watch on deck would be drilled into smartness, encouraged by canes, blows and the rope-ends of the boatswain's mates. They would reef topsails, send up royal-yards aloft, send down topgallant masts, practise anchor-drill or the use of cutlass and musket. Down below on the gun-decks the gunner's mates took their crews through drills and exercises. At four o'clock there was a second serving of grog to wash down the weevil-infested biscuits or cold pea-soup. Shortly before supper the drummer beat a signal to all hands to go to their stations and the ship was inspected by midshipmen and lieutenants. The day ended with the men taking their hammocks from the nettings on deck and the nightwatch set.

Carved stone, Lärbo

Snorre describes the battle of Svold, the bloody encounter in the Sound in about the year 1000 AD, between the Norwegian king Olav Tryggvason's fleet led by the great longship *Ormen Lange* and the combined Danish and Swedish fleets under Sven Forkbeard the Dane and the Swedish king Olof. It was on this occasion that Ejnar Tamberskaelver's bow was shattered. 'Then King Olav said: 'What was that which broke with such a noise?' Ejnar answered: "The kingdom of Norway from your hand, your majesty".' And so it proved, for the Norwegian ships were routed after a hard struggle. Snorre continues; 'They smote both with axe and with sword and threw spears and anything which could be used as a missile; some of them shot with the bow or threw arrows with their hands. So many weapons flew towards the *Ormen* that it was hardly possible to protect oneself with the shield. King Olav's men became so wild and angry that they jumped up on the top strake. Many of them forgot that they were not on dry land and went overboard.' Finally King Olav himself fell from his ship with his shield over him, quickly submerged and was never seen again.

From this and other descriptions of sea battles in the sagas, we can form a picture of sea warfare at the time of the Vik-

Carved stone, Garde

ings. First, stones were collected on board to be used as missiles, and perhaps an extra strake was fitted to the side of the ship as a parapet to afford some protection during the battle. Each man was ordered to arm himself and occupy his allotted station. The sail was lowered and the ships laid together in a *tengsl* (secured stem to stern so that the enemy could not break through the line of battle). Then the battle signal was sounded and the ships were rowed forward against the enemy fleet, most often in a wedge-shaped battle formation. As soon as they came within range the air began to hum with the sound of arrows and stones. If they ventured too near they ran the risk of a grapnel or a boat-hook being got aboard so that the ship could be held fast and boarded for hand-to-hand fighting. In

such a battle a high ship's side was a great advantage. The high-sided cog of the middle ages was originally a merchant vessel, but her sides made her easy to defend against such an attack. On the other hand it proved impossible in certain circumstances for a cog to engage in battle with attackers until the cog's boat had been manned, and the fight taken up at the level of the warship. Even when castles were built both forward and aft on the longships the struggle was still unequal and, about the year 1300, the longship type, after 500 years of faithful service, had to make way for the heavy and slow but more battleworthy cog.

Fresco, Skamstrup church

The battle of Camperdown, 1797

In the event of the marine drummer beating to quarters every man of the *Victory* knew his post. Aloft the topmen secured supplementary rigging to the yards while down below strong rope nettings were hung over the upper-deck to catch any wreckage, or men, falling from aloft. The sails, the boats, and deck equipment were soused with water to reduce their inflammability, buckets of water were stood behind the guns for men to cool themselves, and the canvas hoses were rigged. The decks were moistened with wet sand to give the men a better footing and around the magazine hatches wet felt screens were nailed to minimise the risk of that worst of catastrophes, an explosion in the powder store.

On the gun-decks the crews, led by the gun-captains, cast off the lashings from the guns, struck open the ports and made the armament ready. Round-shot was placed ready and horns full of priming-powder were hung from the deck beams. The galley-fire was put out and silence reigned. Below the gun-decks, in the magazine, the gunner was handing out cartridges to the powder-boys, the surgeon made ready his grim equipment, and marines guarded the hatches against those whose nerve might fail and seek safety in the orlop-deck. The carpenters stood by with material for emergency repairs. Picked men, to act when required as boarders, could be distinguished by their cutlasses, but until ordered they sweated alongside their

mates at the guns. On a well ordered ship all was ready within six minutes of the last drum-beat.

The effective range of the guns was, by modern standards, infinitesimal; a long-barrelled 32-pounder, at an elevation of ten degrees, might reach $1\frac{1}{2}$ miles. Its capacity for accurate shooting was limited; the uncertain casting of the round-shot and the variability of the powder-charge saw to that. An action usually reached its climax with ships battering one another at less than 400 yards range. Should opposing ships grind alongside one another during an engagement the boarding parties were 'called away' to settle the matter with hand-to-hand fighting.

Principally we associate the *Victory* with her part in the

A hand-to-hand fight aboard the Spanish *San Joseph* with Nelson leading the boarding party

battle of Trafalgar against the combined fleets of France and Spain, but by 1805 she was an old ship, a veteran with long sea-service. In 1778, under Admiral Keppel she fought at Ushant, and in 1779 as flag-ship of Sir Charles Hardy the *Victory* led a fleet which stood between Britain and the allied French and Spanish fleets. Kempenfelt flew his flag at her masthead and in 1781 intercepted a French fleet, capturing 15 prizes. It was on the *Victory* that Lord Howe led the relief of Gibraltar in 1783 and met the enemy off Cape Spartel on the African coast in an inconclusive engagement.

A decade later, under Lord Hood, she was involved with the evacuation of Royalist French from Toulon, escorting home the great *Commerce de Marseilles*, the largest ship afloat and dwarfing even the *Victory*. She served long in the Mediterranean, and under Sir John Jervis at the hard-fought battle of St. Vincent in 1797, before returning home and laying-up at Portsmouth. Recommissioned under Nelson, she hunted Villeneuve until the triumphant end of the chase at Trafalgar in 1805. This was not, however, the conclusion of her career at sea: there was arduous convoy work from the Baltic to the Mediterranean ahead, which ended only with the peace in 1815.

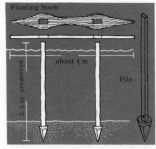

The ancient division of Denmark into hundreds, which is still the basis of the country's division into police districts and certain ecclesiastical areas, rests on traditions which presumably go back to the Migration period. Originally the ship levy seems to have consisted of one ship to be supplied by each hundred. Consequently each of the old hundreds had access to the sea or to a navigable river, if necessary via a 'corridor' which cut across all natural frontiers and parish boundaries. At a later date the hundreds were divided into a number (up to 45) of *skiben*, each of which equipped a ship for the war fleet. Each *skiben* was again divided into a number (up to 42) of *havne*. A *havne* included one or more estates which had to provide the crew to man one of the warship's oars, and it was also the responsibility of the *havne* to provide the necessary equipment, sword, spear and iron helmet, together with provisions for two months, when the fleet was called out. In addition the *havne* had to pay the 'horse tax' and the 'mail tax' to the ship's captain, who had to provide himself with a horse and coat of mail from this and who, moreover, was heavily armed in the manner of a knight. The Danish monarchy, through this institution, had at its disposal, and at the expense of the peasant population, a strong fleet and a force of about 1,000 knights.

On the Bayeux Tapestry we can follow the landing of the horses from William's ships. According to Saxo, King Erik Emune was the first man in Denmark who combined sea warfare with knightly service, 'a custom which posterity has diligently continued to observe'. This change certainly accounts in part for the military superiority of Denmark in the Baltic area in subsequent years, and for the far-reaching change in the social structure, since the knights became established as a social class whilst the land-owning peasants, the fleet's former fighting strength, were reduced to the status of oarsmen and second-rate forces. The war fleet was first and foremost a mobile defence force but, with the Wendish attacks on the Danish coast in the 11th and 12th centuries, it was necessary, to an ever-increasing extent, to resort to purely defensive measures. 'The usual means of countering the pirates was not to defend oneself with arms and with force, but to block the harbour entrances with bulwarks and booms'. (Saxo). Several defensive structures against the Wends have come to light in recent years in the waters around South Jutland, South Fyn, South Zealand and Lolland-Falster. These Danish marine works are now being investigated by underwater archaeologists, and they show that difficult tasks were being accomplished in this field.

Danish marine works

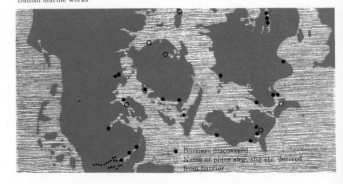

The medieval system of providing a naval force was to call upon the major ports to despatch a previously determined quota of merchant vessels for the king's use. This was gradually superseded by the growth of a permanent force: a navy to be used as and when required. The change had been hastened by the growing specialisation of ships. By the end of the Tudor period it was increasingly difficult for merchantmen to be hastily mustered and within a short time transformed into effective men-of-war, although the practice continued until the re-organisation of the navy under Parliament in 1650.

It was one thing to evolve a Royal Navy, as Charles I did (with fatal enthusiasm). It was quite another to recruit crews to man the ships adequately. Ships might be laid-up with little trouble and then re-commissioned in times of national emergency. But to find crews to man them with equal rapidity, let alone skilled and willing crews, was a problem which defied solution throughout the 17th and 18th centuries – and beyond.

From the day of her commissioning the Victory depended upon brute force to bring her crew to its full strength. Other methods were tried; placards, posters and handbills were used to encourage volunteers. These promised prize-money,

but not details of how it was distributed, good food, without references to weevil-ridden biscuits and coarse salt beef. The outstanding seaworthy qualities of the ship named on the poster were emphasised together with details telling of a bounty of thirty shillings for every volunteer should any further incentive be required. We do not know how many seamen answered the call to form the first crew of the Victory, but out of the 850 officers and men aboard at Trafalgar there were 181 volunteers among the 700 or so ratings. With the name of Nelson to act as a lure it does not seem a large proportion.

The larger fraction had been gathered in a variety of ways. Captured smugglers were sent to the fleet upon conviction and the press-gang worked hard to keep pace with the wastage brought about by death and disease. The press-gang was based at a number

of coastal centres, each under the direction of an impress officer. His principal quarry were the trained seamen of the merchant ships, particularly those from the North East coal trade. Sailors ashore or afloat were liable to be swept up by his patrols, mustered in waiting cutters, and when a sufficient number had accumulated, consigned to the receiving ship at a naval base.

Only the end of hostilities could ensure the discharge of these men and shore-leave was not permitted. If a ship paid-off during war-time the discharged crew could, and often did, find the press-gang waiting for their departure through the dockyard gate. The only concession accorded them was the discharge certificate they carried. This was signed by the captain of their last ship and entitled them to re-instalment at not less than their old rating. But such trained recruits were rare; watermen, longshoremen and fishermen were all valued as suitable material for transformation into jacktars. Various groups of waterside workers subscribed towards bounties, in order to gain a rather tenuous right to exemption from the press-gang.

By the end of the 18th century even these rough and ready expedients to man the fleet were proving inadequate. In 1795 the Quota Act was passed and called for each

Service aboard royal ships meant an absence of two or three years

county to provide men in proportion to its population, a demand later extended to seaport towns. For example, London had to provide 5,704 and all told 30,000 men, many of very questionable potential as seamen, were recruited in this way. They were known to their shipmates as Lord Mayor's Men and the £70 bounty they received upon joining caused resentment among veterans who had volunteered and had been pleased to accept as little as £5.

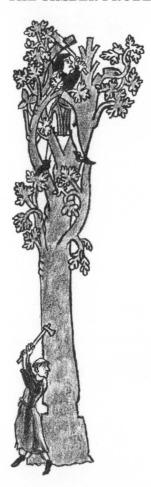

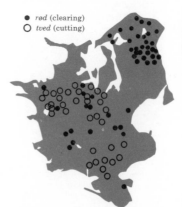

● *rød* (clearing)
○ *tved* (cutting)

Names of settlements on Zealand

The 1,100 ships of the Danish war fleet were always ready, distributed along the coasts, and the ships which were built to take the place of those that were worn out or damaged were probably built in the region in which they were to be used. Warships were apparently kept under cover, in a *naust*, and therefore had a long life when damage at sea was avoided. Given an average lifetime of 25 years, it was necessary for 1,100 divided by 25 = 44 ships to be renewed yearly over the whole country. To judge by the warships in the Skuldelev find, 50–80 cubic metres of timber must have been felled to build a 20-section ship, 20–25 metres in length. The keel needed an oak log of 15–18 metres, and a few similar logs were used for the long midship lengths of the top strakes as well as for the stringers. Shorter and broader logs were chosen for the keelson, the stem and the sternpost, whilst sturdy crooked oak branches were used for ribs and knees. The most difficult thing was to find logs from which to split out the planks. Around the year 1800 the art of splitting an oak log into planks was still well known and a German work on forestry from that period prescribes that 'wood for splitting must be grown sound, straight, clean and from a compact stand'. To which must be added the

important need for the log to be free from the twisted growth which is often found in oak. However, from one long, heavy and suitable log, it was possible to meet all the ship's requirements in planks, as a log can give up to 32 planks. It is otherwise with ash or pine logs, where only two planks can be obtained from each trunk. On the whole the fleet's building programme did not constitute a threat to the wood stocks of the Danish forests as far as quantity was concerned, but it did make great demands on them in respect of quality.

It was a different matter with large military projects such as the building of the Trelleborg 'fortresses'. It is cal-

culated that at least 8,000 large trees, principally oaks, went into the building of Trelleborg, the equivalent of about 85 hectares of wood and, although recent research into the building of the houses indicates a flimsier structure than had originally been assumed, the effect of this building work was clearly noticeable in the nearby forests The same applies to the pile defences; near Hominde in Rødby fjord for example, a 200 metre-long obstruction has been found, consisting of a row of heavy floating booms and a wide area of driven piles as thick as a man's arm, the number of which is estimated at more than 15,000.

Annual increase
44 ships at 12 trees each =
528 trees = 10 hectares

In his book 'Forest and Sea Power', the American historian R.G.Albion examined the difficulties experienced in securing the all-important supplies of timber for ship construction during the period of conflict and expansion, 1652–1862. Even before this Britain's position as a naval power was under the threat of the failure to find raw materials. Shortages of ship-timber and mast-wood forced upon shipwrights the acceptance of inferior materials in times of emergency. The wooden battle-fleet's worst enemies were not the opposing ships round-shot but decay and rot, produced partly by conditions encouraged through construction over-hastily carried out, and partly by half-understood methods of prevention.

Throughout the greater part of the 18th century a vessel was estimated to have an average life, from launching to the first docking for major repairs, of 25–30 years. But this period progressively declined until during the Napoleonic Wars

it was reduced to about eight years. The Victory, unlike many of her contemporaries, was built under the protection of an enormous timber roof to shield the timbers from rain and an over-rapid drying out from sun and wind. Moreover, such protection contributed to the Victory's longevity, for rain water imprisoned in the unventilated cavities and joints of the hull were the inevitable breeding places of rot and decay. Working under cover shipwrights could speed construction and continue at night by the light of naphtha flares.

The shipbuilding programme for the establishment and maintenance of a fleet such as the one of which the Victory was a part consumed whole forests. No less than 300,000 cubic feet of timber went into the Victory while a smaller 74-gun ship needed nearly 2,000 oak trees to be sacrificed for its creation besides elm and fir in large quantities. The administrative machinery of the 18th century was a ramshackle affair and was ill equipped to provide a steady flow of suitable shipbuilding timber while the changing policies of successive governments did little to assist. It resulted in inadequate stocks, shortages of 'compass timber' and the use in shipbuilding of wood which was unseasoned, hurriedly bought and which resulted in structural failure.

The Victory was built in a huge shed

One ship-of-the-line, the Queen Charlotte, built in 1810, had to be reconstructed, because of dry-rot, even before her maiden voyage and only a year after her launch.

In warmer seas, and nearly all vessels saw service in the Mediterranean or West Indian waters at some time, the teredo worm attacked below the water-line. Experiments were made from 1758 onwards with copper-sheathing to prevent this. Eventually it provided the answer, but not before it was realised that contact between copper and iron bolts in the ships hull produced a highly corrosive electrolitic action; for a time the cure was worse than the disease. In 1783 iron bolts were abolished and copper fastenings substituted. This proved so effective that it was generally adopted throughout the Navy and foreign going merchant ships.

45

Boathouse

After the Norwegian king Sverre had built the large ship *Mariasuden* with 32 sections in 1182–83, he found a use for her the following year at the battle of Norefjord, in which the very size of this ship resulted in his being able to defeat King Magnus. After the battle the ships were sailed to Bergen and the *Mariasuden* was pulled ashore and placed under cover. Next autumn they wanted to launch the ship again but she could not be budged. The towns-folk were called together to help, but without any more success. Finally the planks at the stem gave way and they had to abandon the attempt to launch it and, instead, they burnt the now useless vessel to the ground.

This short life is hardly typical for warships, but on the other hand, keeping a ship under cover was probably quite usual. In several places in west Norway sites have been identified by archaeologists of such boathouses or *naust*, and some quite simply have the place-name Longshiphouse (in Norwegian, *Langskibsnøst*), as for example a site near Vikedal in the Sandeidfjord in Ryfylke.

In the autumn–October at the latest–the ship went into winter quarters. She was pulled ashore after the mast had been lowered, and placed in the *naust*. According to the Gulating law this building was a light timber structure built from posts stuck into the ground and joined at the top. The roof was made of rafters joined by thin planks which formed a support for a layer of birch bark and turf. The walls could also be built up of flat stones, laid like a dry wall, or more simply of turf.

The house which has been built for the restored Skuldelev ships on the shores of the fjord at Roskilde is a masterpiece from the drawing board of the architect, Professor Erik Chr. Sørensen, and it is very different from the old *naust*. The five ships are here displayed in a hall of concrete and glass which projects a little into the water so that one has the impression of ships in immediate contact with the water and the landscape of the fjord. Here one can study the ships in all their details as they are reconstructed after their long conservation treatment. Air conditioning sees to it that there is the correct humidity (55%–60%) and temperature (15–20°C) all the year round, so that the ships will be able to remain secure in the hall for all time.

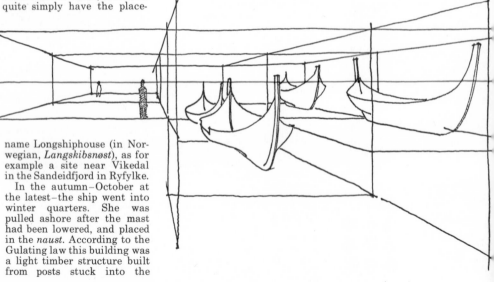

The *Hastings*, a 74 gun ship laid-up on the Medway near the naval base of Chatham

The wooden ships-of-the-line were expensive to maintain and a constant drain upon a country with limited resources and wide commitments. Whenever a short period of peace intervened between the apparently interminable wars of the 18th century the Admiralty was encouraged to take them out of commission. The ships were then laid-up 'in ordinary': that is, they were stripped of their upper yards and masts, their stores and guns were sent ashore for re-entry in the royal dockyard stores and then, if peace seemed assured their decks were covered with a temporary wooden roofing. 'Wind-sails', which were canvas ventilators rigged upon wooden frames above the roofing, assisted in ensuring a flow of air throughout the hull in an attempt to prevent decay gaining a foot-hold in the fabric of the hull. Naval pensioners lived aboard and were expected to maintain a strict routine of pumping-out, lime-washing between-decks, opening ports and hatchways, whilst guarding against the hazards of fire and tending the mooring cables.

Ships out of commission might alternatively be employed as Receiving Ships for newly-pressed men or spend a period, like the *Victory*, moored bow and stern, as a hospital ship or even as a depôt ship for the Army. A grimmer employment for them was to provide accommodation for prisoners-of-war. Later, hulks were used to detain criminals prior to their transhipment to the penal colonies in the Antipodes, or for them to provide unskilled labour for the naval dockyards. Other ships, no longer seaworthy, might be rigged with sheer-legs, great spars fitted with multiple tackles for stepping masts into vessels fitting-out.

Smaller naval craft were pensioned off to become Custom House guard-vessels, anchored in remote creeks and rivers to discourage smuggling. When even this unde-manding duty was beyond them vessels might be stripped to their bare bones and sunk to provide breakwaters or the foundations for fortifications.

With the conclusion of the Napoleonic Wars the great fleet assembled to ensure victory was rapidly dispersed. Many found their way to the ship-breakers yard to be torn apart for the value of the copper fastenings and timber which might be sold for the less testing purpose of house-building. Those that survived were faced with obsolescence, brought about by changes in naval architecture and later by the acceptance of steam-power and new forms of armament, far too heavy for their ageing wooden hulls to support. There were attempts to adapt some to the rapid pace of technological change as the 19th century advanced, but they were limited. The survivors became accommodation hulks at dockyards and the last could still be seen on Thames-side breakers yards in the twentieth century – rapidly reduced to lumber and scrap.

It is fortunate that the *Victory*, because her association with Nelson and his victories enabled her to capture the public imagination, escaped such a fate and is preserved at Portsmouth Dockyard.

Her fighting days over, a ship-of-the-line is employed as a hulk for convicts to live aboard

GLOSSARY

Animal head post found in the Oseberg ship

ANCHOR *Bower:* Anchors which are stowed nearest to the bows. *Kedge:* The smallest of the anchors carried aboard a ship. *Sheet:* The same size and weight as the bower anchors and kept ready bent to a cable for use in an emergency. *Stream:* Smaller than the bower and sheet anchors and used as a temporary mooring or for manoeuvring the ship.

BETWEEN DECKS Any part of the ship below; the space between two decks.

BILGE The flat part of a ship's bottom.

BITTS Large upright baulks of timber, connected some way from their top by a cross piece; over this the bight of the cable is placed. There are smaller bitts fitted at the foot of the mast upon which running rigging, such as the topsail sheets, were belayed.

BOATS Small open vessels of which sea-going ships carried several.

BOTTOMBOARDS Lengths of timber fastened together and laid over the bottom of a boat as flooring.

BRACES Ropes attached to the yard-arms to heave them through a horizontal plane. Also an extra security to the rudder, fixed to the stern post.

BREECHING A strong rope used to secure a cannon and prevent it from recoiling too far when discharged.

BULK-HEADS Partitions in a ship, at right-angles to the keel.

BUTT-END The end of a plank making up a ship's side or decking, uniting with the end of another.

CABLE-TIER The part of the orlop deck where the ship's cables are stored.

CARLINGS Short pieces of timber ranging fore and aft, from one of the deck beams to another and into which they are fitted.

CATHARPINGS Tackles rove between the port and starboard shrouds to keep them taut and to enable the yards to be braced up sharper.

CHANNELS (Chainwales) Strong broad planks bolted to the ship's side to keep the dead-eyes in the chains away from the hull and to spread the rigging away from the mast at a greater and more effective angle.

CLENCH To deform the end of a fastening so that it will not draw out–usually done over a rove.

CLINKER BUILD A form of boatbuilding in which the strakes are placed so that they partly overlap one another–upper strake outboard of lower strake.

CLOSE-FIGHTS Bulk-heads erected fore-and-aft in the ship, for the men to stand behind in close engagements and use small-arms.

COAMINGS The sides of a hatch raised above the level of the deck.

COMPASS TIMBER The curved growths, often derived from hedgerow oaks, suited to the making of the frames.

DEAD-EYES A circular block with three eyes in it which receive the landyards of a shroud or stay and facilitate its setting up; 'dead' because it does not revolve.

DRIVER A large fore-and-aft sail, suspended from a gaff and carried on the mizzen mast, also termed a spanker.

FLUSH LAID A form of boat building where the strakes abut edge to edge without overlap.

GANG-WAY A platform reaching from the ship's quarter-deck to the fore-castle on each side; also the place where a person enters the ship.

GASKET A plaited cord fastened to the yards and used to secure a furled sail by wrapping it round. Gaskets were fitted at the centre, quarters and extremities of the yard.

GRIPE A piece of timber which joins the keel to the cutwater; also to make lee-way when sailing.

HALYARDS Tackles or ropes to hoist the yards when setting sail.

HORSE A rope made fast below the yard-arm on which men stand when handling sail; also a length of timber, iron or rope fixed across the deck upon which the sheet of a fore-and-aft sail travels.

JURY MASTS Temporary masts, improvised when others are shot or carried away.

KEELSON A length of wood fitted over the ribs to distribute vertical loads over a greater length of the boat.

KNEES Timber grown to shape and used to strengthen the sides of a boat.

LUBBER A sailor who does not know his duty; hence lubber-holes, square apertures in the tops through which the less agile may gain entrance when going aloft.

MANGER A small area, extending athwart the lower-deck of a ship of war, immediately within the hawse-holes and fenced by the manger-board which prevented seas from washing aft through the hawse-holes.

MESSENGER A rope attached to the anchor-cable and passed round the capstan by which the anchor is heaved up.

NIPPERS Plaited rope used to bind the cable temporarily to the messengers.

ORLOP DECK The lowest deck of the ship, lying on the beams of the hold: the cables are coiled here and the stores kept.

PAY To rub tar or pitch, etc. on anything with a brush.

PAY OFF To make a ship's head recede from the wind by backing the head-sails, etc. When getting under way the ship's boats might be launched to assist in this.

PREVENTER Anything for temporary security in the rigging, e.g. a preventer brace.

QUARTER That part of the ship's side between the mizzen chains and the stern. Also the respective corners at the stern of a vessel.

QUARTER SAWN Timber converted into boards in such a way that the growth rings meet the face in any part at an angle greater than or equal to 45°.

RABBET A groove or channel worked in a member to accept another, without a lip being formed.

RATLE DOWN To fix ratline on shrouds and topmast shrouds, i.e. short lengths of line secured across at intervals to form a ladder.

RIBS A simple form of transverse member extending across the boat, set against the planking.

SCARF A tapered or wedge-shaped joint between pieces of similar section at the join.